Dinosaurs

Credits:

Publisher: Twin Sisters Productions, LLC
Executive Producers: Kim Mitzo Thompson,
Karen Mitzo Hilderbrand
Words and Music by: Kim Mitzo Thompson,
Karen Mitzo Hilderbrand, Hal Wright
Workbook Author: Ken Carder
Illustrator: Lon Eric Craven
Workbook Design: Steven Dewitt

ISBN-13: 978-157583-8960
www.twinsisters.com

What Is a Dinosaur?

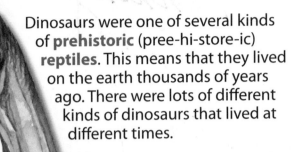

Dinosaurs were one of several kinds of **prehistoric** (pree-hi-store-ic) **reptiles**. This means that they lived on the earth thousands of years ago. There were lots of different kinds of dinosaurs that lived at different times.

Dinosaurs were reptiles. Most hatched from eggs. No dinosaurs could fly and none lived in the water.

Some dinosaurs walked on two legs. They are called **bipeds** (bye-peds). Some dinosaurs walked on four legs. They are called **quadrupeds** (quad-roo-peds). Some dinosaurs were able to do both. Some were speedy and some were slow.

Some dinosaurs had thick **armor** plating, some had **horns**, and some had **spikes**. Some dinosaurs had thick, bumpy skin, and some even had a form of feathers.

The largest dinosaurs were over 100 feet long and up to 50 feet tall. The smallest dinosaurs were about the size of a chicken. Most dinosaurs were somewhere in the middle.

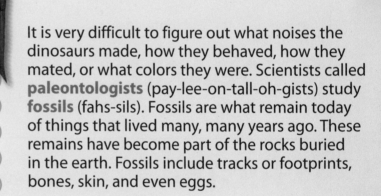

Most dinosaurs were **herbivores** (her-bih-vores). This means they ate plants. The three-horned dinosaur Triceratops was an herbivore.

Some dinosaurs were **carnivores** (car-nih-vores). This means they ate meat. The huge dinosaur Tyrannosaurus rex was a carnivore.

Dinosaurs mysteriously went **extinct** (ex-stink-t). This means that they have all died and are gone forever. Scientists have many **theories**, or ideas, about what happened to the dinosaurs. No one knows for sure what caused the dinosaurs to die out.

It is very difficult to figure out what noises the dinosaurs made, how they behaved, how they mated, or what colors they were. Scientists called **paleontologists** (pay-lee-on-tall-oh-gists) study **fossils** (fahs-sils). Fossils are what remain today of things that lived many, many years ago. These remains have become part of the rocks buried in the earth. Fossils include tracks or footprints, bones, skin, and even eggs.

Who Named the Dinosaurs?

The word dinosaur means *fearfully great lizard*. A scientist named Sir Richard Owen from Great Britain first used the word *dinosaur* in 1842. In Greek, *deinos* means *fearfully great* and *sauros* means *lizard*.

Dinosaurs are named by the people who discover the fossils or by the paleontologist who determines that the fossils represent a new kind of dinosaur. Sometimes, the dinosaur's name describes something unusual about its body, head, or feet. Some are named for the location where they are found. And some dinosaurs are named for the way scientists think the dinosaurs behaved. The names have to be approved by the International Commission on Zoological Nomenclature.

Dinosaur Scramble

The clues will help you unscramble the following words.

SPTREILE Dinosaurs belonged to this group of animals.

Reptiles

ISONALEOTTPLOG This scientist studies dinosaurs and other fossils.

LIFOSSS All that remain of the dinosaurs bodies today are these hard, rock-like objects.

VOBRHERIE Most dinosaurs ate plants.

NIVOCARRE Some dinosaurs were meat-eaters.

TXNICTE All the dinosaurs have died and are gone forever.

PEDBI Some dinosaurs walked on two legs.

DPEDRUQUA Some dinosaurs walked on four legs.

ULFRFEALY REGAT ZLIRDA (3 Words) The meaning of the word *dinosaur*.

4

When I Grow Up I Want To Be A Paleontologist

#1

(Chorus)

When I grow up I want to be
   something very interesting.
The job I'll do will help a lot of people,
   and I'll like the work that I do.
Each day will be adventurous, and
   I'll strive to learn a lot.
Then I'll share what I know
   and my knowledge will grow.
It's the perfect, perfect job!

I just love to learn about dinosaurs! I think I want to become a paleontologist. A paleontologist studies the remains of prehistoric life and fossils. I want to go on dinosaur digs and look for the bones of Tyrannosaurus rex. I could do research, study the fossils found from long ago, or help create realistic dinosaurs to be displayed at museums. What a great occupation!

Now science is important,
   so I'll study hard when learning about biology.
Experiments in chemistry will
   help me learn to develop good hypotheses.
Then I'll read and I'll read and I'll read some more,
   and I'll share just what I learn.
'Cause when I grow up I want to
   be something very interesting.

(Chorus)

Yes, I'll share what I know
   and my knowledge will grow.
It's the perfect, perfect job!
The perfect, perfect job!

Words and Music by: Kim Mitzo Thompson,
Karen Mitzo Hilderbrand, Hal Wright

Where Did All The Dinosaurs Go?

#2

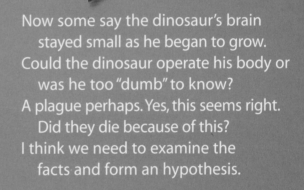

Where did all the dinosaurs go?
I wish they were still around.
Where did all the dinosaurs go?
The answer can't be found.
And though some theories
do make sense scientists don't agree.
About what caused this mystery
It's the dinosaur catastrophe.

Now some will say that mammals
took the eggs right from the nest.
So the dinosaurs they never hatched
because of these strange pests,
While others think a nasty plague
caused the dinosaurs to die—
But these seem so unlikely, that we
still are asking why.

Could the earth have been struck
from a comet from outer space?
Creating a thick dark dust
which blocked the sun from the
dinosaur's face?
Did they really get that cold?
Did the plants die then?
Did they have enough to eat?
Though some think so, the theories,
you know are very incomplete.

(Chorus)

Now some say the dinosaur's brain
stayed small as he began to grow.
Could the dinosaur operate his body or
was he too "dumb" to know?
A plague perhaps. Yes, this seems right.
Did they die because of this?
I think we need to examine the
facts and form an hypothesis.

Maybe the plant eaters ate the
flowering plants and all the ferns.
And then there was no food
which caused the dinosaurs concern.
The plant eaters died and then
the meat eaters had no food to eat.
So then the meat eaters died
because they like to eat fresh meat.

(Chorus)

It's the dinosaur catastrophe.
It's the dinosaur catastrophe!

Words and Music by: Kim Mitzo Thompson,
Karen Mitzo Hilderbrand, Hal Wright

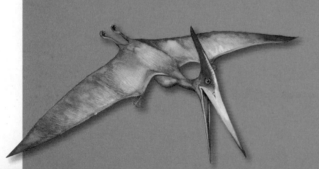

Let's Go On A Dinosaur Dig!

#3

Let's go on a dinosaur dig.
　　What tools should I bring?
I know I'll need a camera
　　to take pictures of everything.
A tape measure I will use
　　to check the distances between
The fossils I find on the ground
　　or by a big ravine.

My dad will bring his jackhammer
　　to remove those large hard rocks
And a geological hammer
　　that will help him with smaller spots
I will use a little brush
　　to remove some sand and dust—
Once the rock has been removed
　　this tool is quite a must.

If we find a fragile bone
　　I know just what to do.
We'll wrap the bone in foil or
　　maybe some tissue.
Some plaster of paris we will add
　　in order to protect the bone
from breaking while we
　　try to complete this tough project.

A magnifying glass I'll take
　　and keep right by my side
I'll look at teeth or small fossils
　　that I hope we will find.
Now if we find a huge amount
　　of fossils in the ground,
We might need ropes and pulleys
　　to move them all around.

Let's go on a dinosaur dig.
　　I know what tools I'll bring.
Let's go on a dinosaur dig
　　with supplies and everything.
Let's go on a dinosaur dig;
　　my tools are now all packed.
A paleontologist I will be.
　　I think I have the knack!

Words and Music by: Kim Mitzo Thompson,
Karen Mitzo Hilderbrand, Hal Wright

I Found A Fossil

Going on a hike is so much fun.
　　Collecting rocks, some weigh a ton.
You won't believe the things I've found
　　When I look closely all around.
Fossils that have been made by shells
　　Or bones or plants, I have to tell—
That fossils help us learn and know,
　　About the things from long ago.

When an animal died long ago, the remains were covered by mud or sand and preserved. After many years it changed to rock. When we find a fossil today it might be the remains of a plant or shell or even an animal.

Now fossil remains of dinosaurs
　　Let us know a whole lot more
Than we ever would without these clues,
　　Let's go on a fossil rendezvous.
Some fossils are preserved in tar or coal.
　　You might see parts or even the whole—
Outline of a leaf or a strange insect,
　　preserved in amber quite perfect.

We use fossils everyday. Fossil fuels such as coal, oil and natural gas burn to make heat and electricity. All of these fossil fuels come from the remains of plants and animals from long ago that have been altered over time by heat and pressure.

Yes, fossils help us learn and know
　　About the things from long ago.
It's like learning a little history,
　　Most scientists they would agree.
So if you like the great outdoors
　　And rocks and streams you do explore—
Start hunting for the old remains
　　And hardened fossils you'll obtain.

Words and Music by: Kim Mitzo Thompson,
Karen Mitzo Hilderbrand, Hal Wright

It's The Three-Horned Dinosaur

Triceratops means three-horned face.
  Do you know what it's famous for?
Yes, three sharp horns upon its head,
  It's the three-horned dinosaur.

Now above each eye there was a horn
  and one right on its nose.
What was the purpose of these horns?
  Protection I suppose.

A bony frill was around its head
  to protect it from attack.
And scaly thick skin covered
  this tough dinosaur's back.

Triceratops liked to eat green plants
  for it was a herbivore.
It used its parrot-like hard beak—
  this massive dinosaur.

With hundreds of sharp teeth
  with which to chew,
Triceratops did eat and eat and eat,
  you wouldn't call Triceratops petite.

(Chorus)

On each front foot it had three hooves
  plus two more extra toes.
It walked so hard along the ground—
  this was not twinkle toes.

On each back foot it had four toes
  each with a hoof they say.
And pads just like rhinoceroses
  have on their feet today.

Triceratops it roamed with friends
  along the countryside.
The babies stayed close to the herd
  or by their mother's side.

For Tyrannosaurus rex behind the trees
  he would watch and wait—
For one to wander close enough
  to be his dinner date.

(Chorus)

It's the three-horned dinosaur.
It's the three-horned dinosaur!

Words and Music by: Kim Mitzo Thompson,
Karen Mitzo Hilderbrand, Hal Wright

Tyrannosaurus rex Didn't Get His Supper

#6

Tyrannosaurus rex—don't forget,
    was the meanest thing around.
That big bully would scare
    all the dinosaurs in town!
With teeth as sharp as razors,
    they all ran far away.
And Tyrannosaurus rex,
    he didn't get his supper for that day!

"King of the tyrant lizards"—
    the meanest thing around.
As long as two school buses
    it stalked across the ground.

It's teeth were sharp and jagged—
    a fearsome awful sight.
With jaws so huge it could have
    swallowed you in just one bite.

It used its tail for balance
    as it roamed across the land.
Walking on its back legs
    respect it would command.

Its eyes faced forward helping it
    to focus on its prey.
With a mighty roar its nasty temper
    it would display.

(Chorus)

It had big feet with four toes,
    but one was turned around.
In fact this backwards toe
    it didn't even touch the ground.

The front legs were a little shorter
    but they had long sharp claws.
To eat they were not needed
    for Rex used his mighty jaws.

This warrior was a creature
    that was feared by big and small.
It could grow as long as forty feet
    and could be eighteen feet tall.

I'm sure it had no friends with
    which to run and play.
For most dinosaurs they knew they
    should stay very far away.

(Chorus)

And Tyrannosaurus rex, he didn't
    get his supper for that day

Words and Music by: Kim Mitzo Thompson,
Karen Mitzo Hilderbrand, Hal Wright

What Color Were The Dinosaurs?

I think that dinosaurs were red
   With splashes of purple on their heads.
Perhaps their bodies had white spots—
   Or pink and blue small polka dots.

Imagine Stegosaurus now
   with brown spots like a milking cow.
Or Brontosaurus, was she pink with
   orange toes? What do you think?

(Chorus)

**I guess we'll never really know,
   For dinosaurs lived long ago.
But brown and green won't do for me.
   I think their colors were extreme.**

Tyrannosaurus he was mean.
   Was he brown, or was he green?
Or maybe like the zebra he
   Had black and white stripes. Could this be?

Triceratops had three huge horns.
   Were they brown like prickly thorns?
I think their three horns looked just like
   A scary tiger's, big and white.

Words and Music by: Kim Mitzo Thompson,
Karen Mitzo Hilderbrand, Hal Wright

(Chorus)

Now stop and think about the way
   The animals look today.
Some have stripes, some are white.
   Each kind is such a special sight.

So when I draw huge dinosaurs,
   I choose three colors, maybe four
And paint them bright. Now I suppose
   That scientists would not oppose.

(Chorus)

11

I'm Not A Dinosaur

#8

Pteranodon I am called,
I'm not a dinosaur.
But I belong to a family—
we are flying Pterosaurs.
This special group of flying reptiles
really is unique.
For we are winged and toothless
and we have long sharp beaks.

Pteranodon, Pteranodon,
I'm not a dinosaur.
But fly I do with my family—
we're flying Pterosaurs.
I weigh about thirty pounds;
I'm small but look at me.
For when my wings are all outstretched
they're twenty-seven feet.

Did you know that Pteranodon did not have a tail? When it flew
in the air Pteranodon had to pay attention to the movements that
it made with its wings and body in order to stay balanced.

Now look real close and notice
on my head there is a crest.
Yes, it will grow to six feet long.
It really is the best.
I glide around the waters and
I search for lots of fish.
And scoop real low and pluck
them out—a tasty little dish.

(Chorus)

Words and Music by: Kim Mitzo Thompson,
Karen Mitzo Hilderbrand, Hal Wright

I Am Stegosaurus

I am Stegosaurus;
   "Roof Lizard" is my name
For on my back are bony plates
   which have brought me fame.
Scientists are puzzled—
   what purpose do they serve?
Do they help protect me
   from intruders I observe?

My legs are quite impressive.
   Look close and you will see,
For twice as long my back legs stand
   than my front legs stand on me.
I feed on vegetation
   as my mouth looks like a beak.
In the back are rows of tiny teeth
   which I know are weak.

I am Stegosaurus—
   with a secret to unveil.
Did you know that four sharp spikes
   sit upon my tail?
I protect myself—
   swish my tail at the enemy,
And hope he'll get the message
   that his supper I will not be.

They say I am not smart
   because my brain is very small.
And that my brain resembles
   the size of a golf ball.
But I am Stegosaurus
   and I'm fine the way I am—
For when I sense grave danger
   I know it's time to scram.

I like to stay close by my friends,
   for safe I want to stay.
For hungry Allosaurus
   lurks behind the trees today.
He waits for me to lag behind
   so he could soon attack.
But I'm too smart and won't be
   Allosaurus' next snack.

I am Stegosaurus;
   "Roof Lizard" is my name
For on my back are bony plates
   which have brought me fame.
Scientists are puzzled—
   should I tell them what they're for?
No, I think I'll keep them guessing
   a little while more.

Words and Music by: Kim Mitzo Thompson,
Karen Mitzo Hilderbrand, Hal Wright

The Brachiosaurus Rap

#10

Man, this dinosaur weighs a lot,
   about 85 tons, they say.
And long, oh yes, about 85 feet
   when measured yesterday.
Some paleontologists found some bones
   in Africa—a continent.
And learned a lot about this
   massive beast, a great accomplishment.

Brachiosaurus he stands so tall,
   about forty-three feet high.
It's longer than a school bus, taller than giraffes
   plus, heavy—my, oh my.
Its front legs were longer than its back legs,
   so scientists proclaim
That "Arm Lizard" will be this
   awesome dinosaur's full name.

It ate green plants—you bet it ate—
   some tons and tons of food.
For if this herbivore went hungry,
   could you imagine his bad mood?
They roamed in groups, or families,
   and watched the little one
In case a hungry meat-eater
   decided to have one for lunch.

Brachiosaurus had a nose
   located above his eyes—
and right on the top of his head that nose
   was used to breathe and sigh.
He may have snorted in a friendly way
   in order to communicate.
Or simply breathe without a pause
   while Brachiosaurus ate.

Yes, Brachiosaurus was one of the
   largest dinosaurs to walk on earth.
Paleontologists continue to study and
   conduct precise research.
For learning about these massive
   beasts takes time and patience too.
But well-worth the effort when we
   learn how big Brachiosaurus grew.

Words and Music by: Kim Mitzo Thompson,
Karen Mitzo Hilderbrand, Hal Wright

Plesiosaurus, Do You Like To Swim?

**Plesiosaurus, do you like to swim
in the deep, deep sea?
Your long, long neck it comes up
to the top for you to breathe.
Your round, round body looks
just like a barrel that is full—
As you swim along to find some
food you look just wonderful.**

Plesiosaurus has four flippers
to dive down in the deep.
Its toes are webbed so we just say
it has four flipper feet.
The overlapping teeth
Plesiosaurus then will use
—To trap its meal—
those fish I'm sure become very confused.

*Plesiosaurus swam in prehistoric oceans. Its name means
"near-reptile" because paleontologists thought that it
resembled a reptile. Plesiosaurus had a unique barrel-shaped body
and a very long neck. Its snake-like neck would twist and turn while
it hunted for food.*

Plesiosaurus needs to watch out
as it swims on by
For Ichthyosaurus likes to munch,
this creature is not shy.
So keep alert and look around
as the enemy is near.
For Plesiosaurus we want you safe
as you are very dear.

(Chorus)
-

Words and Music by: Kim Mitzo Thompson,
Karen Mitzo Hilderbrand, Hal Wright

Good Things Come In Small Packages

#12

Good things come in
   small packages, small packages—
Big is not always better.
If you're small you can
   fit in tight places—
Squeeze into very small spaces,
Especially if you need to hide!

*For instance, if you lived long ago with Allosaurus like I did you really would
be glad if you were small. Oh, let me introduce myself. I am Compsognathus (comp-sog-
NATH-us) and I am only about two feet long, about the size of a
chicken. I have three toes on my legs and two fingers on my hands. I like to
eat meat, especially small lizards. And...I'm glad that I am small!*

Compsognathus is my name
   and I am very small.
My body is covered with feathers
   and I'm not very tall.
They say I'm the size of a pigeon
   or maybe even a chicken.
I run and hide from Allosaurus
   for he is not my friend.

(Chorus)

*Yes, and sometimes we really needed to hide. Hi, I'm, Saltopus
(SAL-tuh-pus). My name means "leaping foot." They say I'm about
the same size as a cat for I only weigh two pounds. I think I'm as
fast and clever as a cat too.   And...I'm glad that I am small!*

Saltopus is my name
   and I am very small.
I have a long neck and large eyes
   but I'm not very tall.
I am fast, I need to be...
   on my hind legs I run.
I like to eat small lizards
   for me they can't outrun.

(Chorus)

Words and Music by: Kim Mitzo Thompson, Karen Mitzo Hilderbrand, Hal Wright

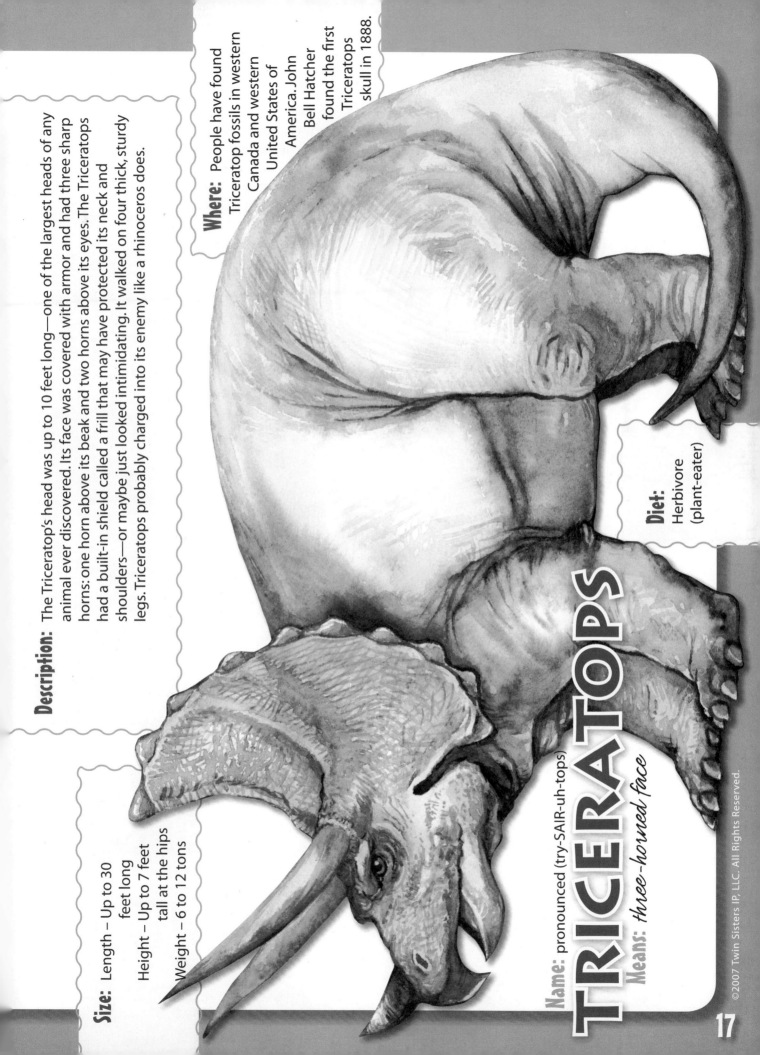

Description: The Triceratops's head was up to 10 feet long—one of the largest heads of any animal ever discovered. Its face was covered with armor and had three sharp horns: one horn above its beak and two horns above its eyes. The Triceratops had a built-in shield called a frill that may have protected its neck and shoulders—or maybe just looked intimidating. It walked on four thick, sturdy legs. Triceratops probably charged into its enemy like a rhinoceros does.

Where: People have found Triceratop fossils in western Canada and western United States of America. John Bell Hatcher found the first Triceratops skull in 1888.

Diet: Herbivore (plant-eater)

Size: Length – Up to 30 feet long

Height – Up to 7 feet tall at the hips

Weight – 6 to 12 tons

Name: pronounced (try-SAIR-uh-tops)

TRICERATOPS

Means: *three-horned face*

Description:

Tyrannosaurus rex wasn't the biggest dinosaur, but it was huge. However, its arms were only about 3 feet long, and it had two-fingered hands. Tyrannosaurus rex had 50 sharp, cone-shaped teeth—some the size of a banana.

Because its arms were short and its eyes were small, some paleontologists believe Tyrannosaurus rex may not have been a fierce, savage predator. It might have been a scavenger. This means that it ate animals that were already dead. Tyrannosaurus rex may have bullied or scared away carnivorous dinosaurs after they had killed their prey. Then, it would have stolen their food.

Where: Someone found the first Tyrannosaurus rex in Hell Creek, Montana. People have found a total of 30 incomple fossils of Tyrannosaurus rex in the United States of America, Canada, and Mongolia. People have even found Tyrannosaurus rex dung

Diet:
Carnivore
(meat-eater)

Size:
Length – 40 feet long
Height – 15 to 20 feet tall
Weight – 5 to 7 tons

Name: pronounced
(tye-RAN-uh-SAWR-us)

TYRANNOSAURUS REX

Means: *tyrant lizard king*

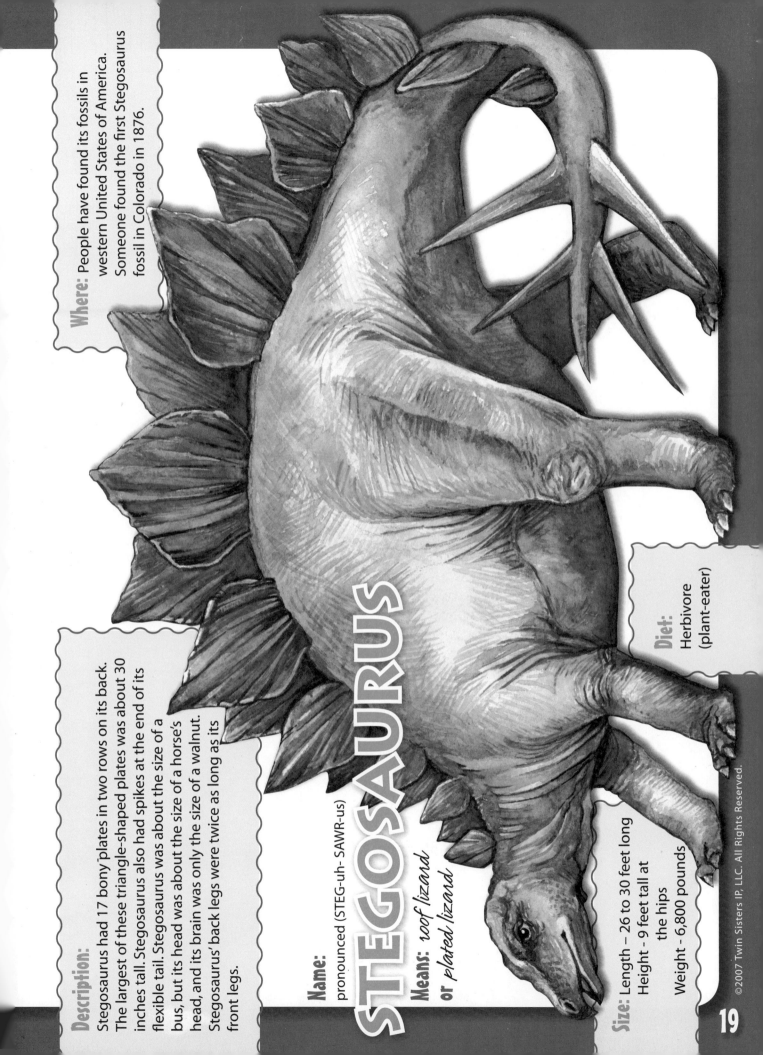

Description:
Stegosaurus had 17 bony plates in two rows on its back. The largest of these triangle-shaped plates was about 30 inches tall. Stegosaurus also had spikes at the end of its flexible tail. Stegosaurus was about the size of a bus, but its head was about the size of a horse's head, and its brain was only the size of a walnut. Stegosaurus' back legs were twice as long as its front legs.

Name:
pronounced (STEG-uh- SAWR-us)

STEGOSAURUS

Means: *roof lizard* *or plated lizard*

Diet: Herbivore (plant-eater)

Size: Length – 26 to 30 feet long
Height - 9 feet tall at the hips
Weight - 6,800 pounds

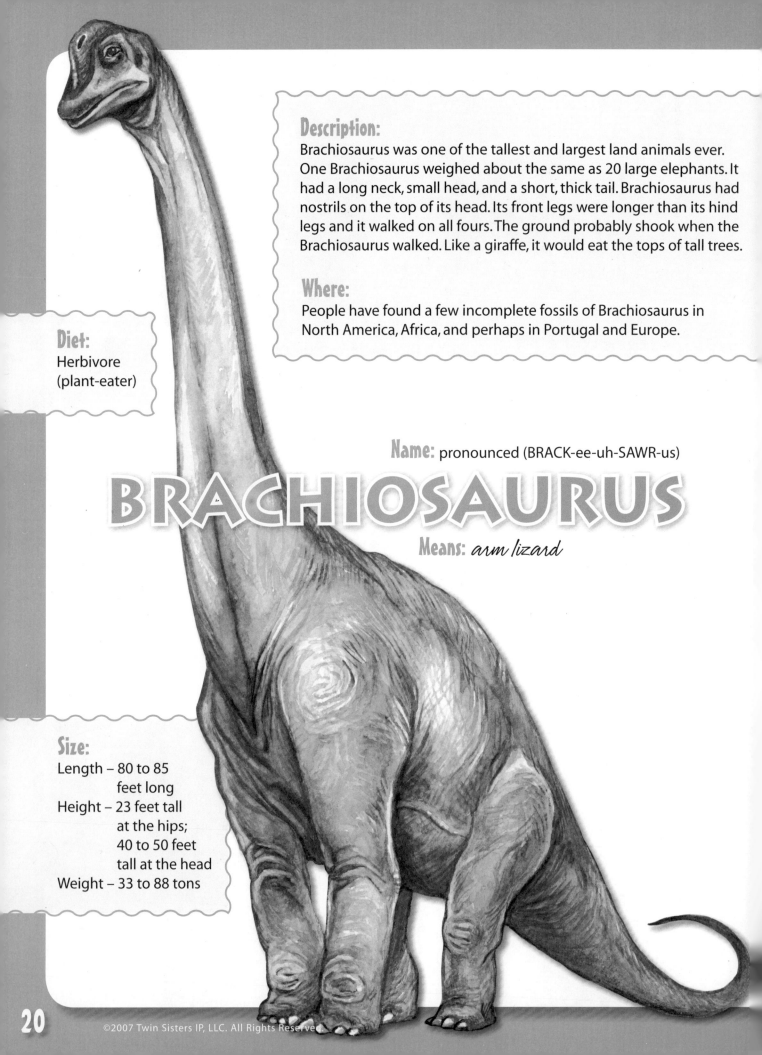

Description:

Brachiosaurus was one of the tallest and largest land animals ever. One Brachiosaurus weighed about the same as 20 large elephants. It had a long neck, small head, and a short, thick tail. Brachiosaurus had nostrils on the top of its head. Its front legs were longer than its hind legs and it walked on all fours. The ground probably shook when the Brachiosaurus walked. Like a giraffe, it would eat the tops of tall trees.

Where:

People have found a few incomplete fossils of Brachiosaurus in North America, Africa, and perhaps in Portugal and Europe.

Diet:

Herbivore
(plant-eater)

Name: pronounced (BRACK-ee-uh-SAWR-us)

BRACHIOSAURUS

Means: *arm lizard*

Size:

Length – 80 to 85
    feet long
Height – 23 feet tall
    at the hips;
    40 to 50 feet
    tall at the head
Weight – 33 to 88 tons

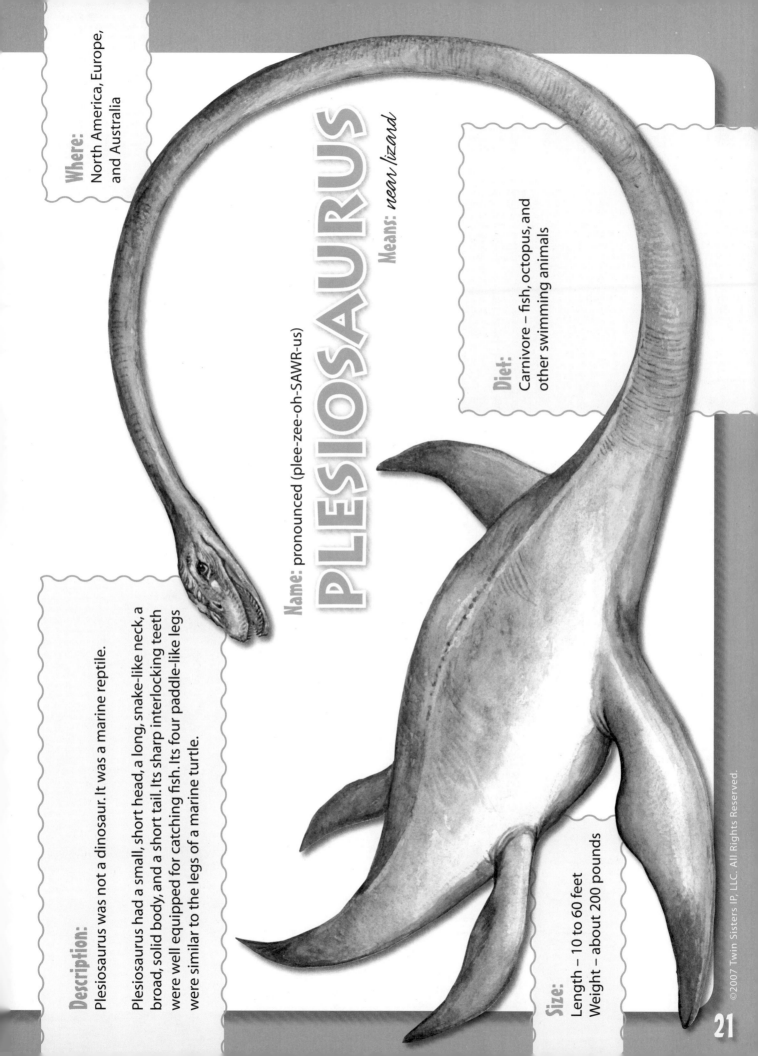

Name: pronounced (plee-zee-oh-SAWR-us)

PLESIOSAURUS

Means: *near lizard*

Diet:
Carnivore – fish, octopus, and other swimming animals

Description:
Plesiosaurus was not a dinosaur. It was a marine reptile.

Plesiosaurus had a small, short head, a long, snake-like neck, a broad, solid body, and a short tail. Its sharp interlocking teeth were well equipped for catching fish. Its four paddle-like legs were similar to the legs of a marine turtle.

Size:
Length – 10 to 60 feet
Weight – about 200 pounds

Name: pronounced (komp-sog-NAY-thus)

COMPSOGNATHUS

Means: *pretty jaw*

Description:
Compsognathus is one of the smallest-known dinosaurs. It was about the size of a chicken. Compsognathus walked on two long, thin legs. It had three-toed feet, a small, pointed head, small, sharp teeth, hollow bones, and a long, flexible neck. Compsognathus had short arms with two clawed fingers on each hand. Its long tail helped it to stay balanced as it moved.

Where:
People have found its fossils in Germany and France

Size:
Length – 2 to 5 feet long
Height – 10 inches tall at the hips
Weight – 6 ½ pounds

Diet:
Carnivore (meat-eater)

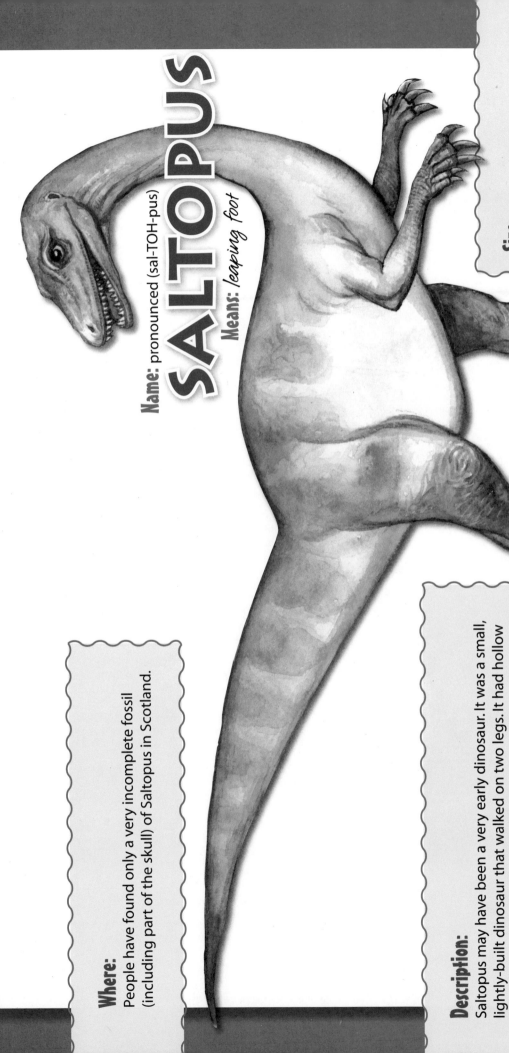

Name: pronounced (sal-TOH-pus)

SALTOPUS

Means: *leaping foot*

Size:
Length – 2 feet long
Height – 8 inches tall at the hips
Weight – 2 pounds

Diet: Carnivore (meat-eater)

Where:
People have found only a very incomplete fossil (including part of the skull) of Saltopus in Scotland.

Description:
Saltopus may have been a very early dinosaur. It was a small, lightly-built dinosaur that walked on two legs. It had hollow bones, a long head, and dozens of small, sharp teeth. Saltopus had five fingers on each hand, but the fourth and fifth fingers on both hands were very small.

PTERANODON

Name: pronounced (ter-AN-oh-don)

Means: *winged and toothless*

Size:
Wingspan – 25 to 30 feet long
Standing Height - 6 feet tall at the hips
Weight - 55 pounds

Diet:
Carnivore (meat-eater)

Description:
Pteranodon was not a dinosaur. It was a flying reptile that lived during the time of the dinosaurs. Pteranodon's wing-span is longer than the wing-span of any known bird. It had a crest on its head, and no teeth at all.

Where:
Someone found the first Pteranodon skull on May 2, 1876 in the Smoky Hill River, which is in Wallace County, Kansas. Fossils have also been found in England.

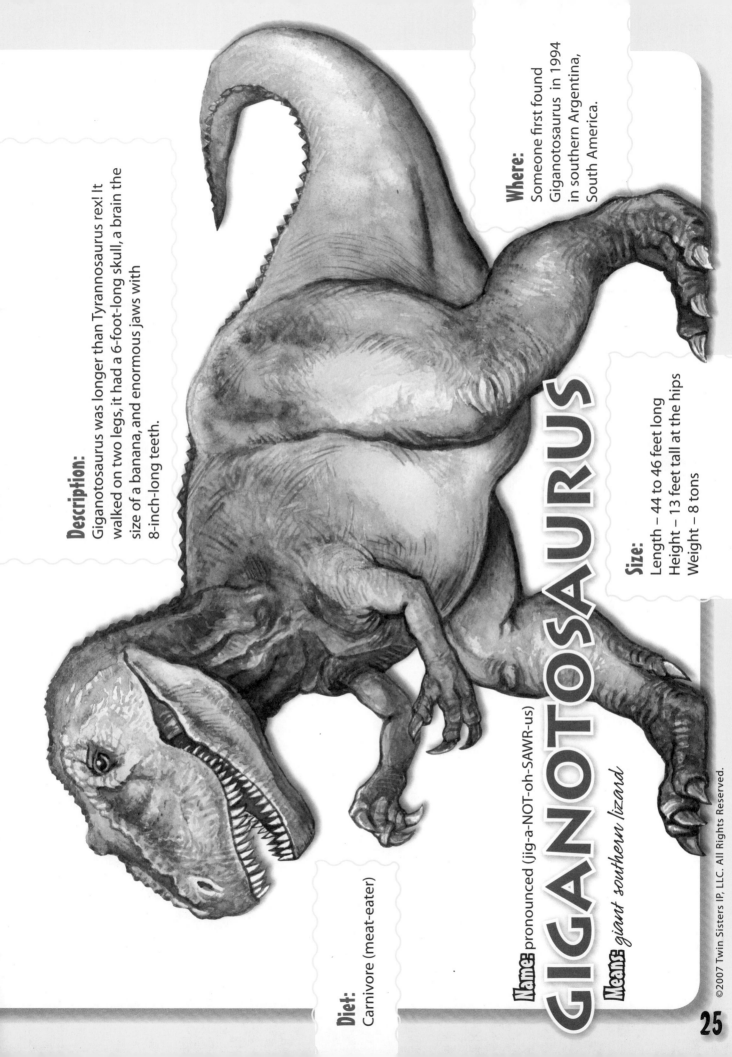

Description:

Giganotosaurus was longer than Tyrannosaurus rex! It walked on two legs, it had a 6-foot-long skull, a brain the size of a banana, and enormous jaws with 8-inch-long teeth.

Where:

Someone first found Giganotosaurus in 1994 in southern Argentina, South America.

Size:

Length – 44 to 46 feet long
Height – 13 feet tall at the hips
Weight – 8 tons

Name: pronounced (jig-a-NOT-oh-SAWR-us)

GIGANOTOSAURUS

Means: *giant southern lizard*

Diet:
Carnivore (meat-eater)

Description:

Ichthyosaurus was not a dinosaur. It was a marine reptile. Ichthyosaurus had sharp teeth, long jaws, and big eyes. It had four crescent-shaped fins, a dorsal fin, and a fish-like tail. Ichthyosaurus breathed air through nostrils which were close to the eyes near the top of the snout. It had to come to the surface of the water to breathe air.

Ichthyosaurus gave birth to live young. Fossils of Ichthyosaurus have been found with babies in its abdomen.

ICHTHYOSAURUS

Name: pronounced (ick-thee-oh-SAWR-us)

Means: *fish lizard*

Where:
People have found Ichthyosaurus fossils in North and South America and in Europe.

Size:
Length – 7 to 30 feet
Weight – about 200 pounds

Diet:
Carnivore – fish, octopus, and other swimming animals

Description:
Allosaurus was a predator with a huge head, an S-shaped neck, short arms, three-fingered hands, and sharp claws that were up to 6 inches long. It had two short horns as well as bony knobs and ridges above its eyes and on the top of its head. It had large, powerful jaws with sharp teeth that were 2 to 4 inches long. Allosaurus got its name from its unusual backbone. The bones in its back were lighter than the bones of other dinosaurs.

Where:
People have found over 60 Allosaurus fossils in places such as western United States of America, Portugal, Europe, Africa, and Australia. Someone discovered the first almost complete Allosaurus skeleton in Colorado in 1883.

Diet:
Carnivore (meat-eater)

Size:
Length - about 40 feet long
Height - 10 feet tall at the hips
Weight - up to 4½ tons

ALLOSAURUS

Name: pronounced (AL-oh-SAWR-us)

Means: *different lizard*

Description:

Quetzalcoatlus was a flying reptile. It was the largest flying animal ever found. It had hollow bones, a small body, and its legs and neck were very long. Quetzalcoatlus had a large brain and big eyes. Its body may have been covered with fur or fuzz. A leather-like membrane covered Quetzalcoatlus' wings, which were nearly 9 inches thick at the elbow.

Where:

Someone found the first Quetzalcoatlus fossil in Big Bend National Park, Texas.

QUETZALCOATLUS

Name: pronounced (KWET-zal-koh-AT-lus)

named after the Aztec feathered god Quetzalcoat

Size:

Wingspan – Nearly 36 feet long!
Neck – 10 feet long
Legs – 7 feet long
Weight – Up to 300 pounds

Diet:

Carnivore – skimmed the water to find prey

28

Size:
Length – 25 to 35 feet long
Height - 4 feet tall at the hips
Weight – 3 to 5 tons

Where:
Ankylosaurus fossils have been found in the western United States and Canada.

Description:
Scientists describe Anklyosaurus as a walking tank! Its body, head, and tail were covered with hard, bony plates. Rows of short spikes protected each side of its body. Its tail was short and thick and ended in a bony club. It had two large horns on each side of its head.

Diet:
Herbivore (plant-eater) - Ankylosaurus had to eat a huge amount of plants to survive so its stomach must have been very large.

ANKYLOSAURUS

Name: pronounced (ang-KIE-lo-SAWR-us)

Means: fused lizard

29

APATOSAURUS

Name: pronounced (a-PAT-o-SAWR-us)

Means: *deceptive lizard*

Where:
Fossils have been found in western United States.

Diet:
Herbivore (plant-eater)

Description:
Apatosaurus used to be called "Brontosaurus," which means "thunder lizard." The Apatosaurus had a small head on a very long neck. Apatosaurus' nostrils were located on the top of its head, and its brain was about the size of a large apple. Apatosaurus defended itself by whipping its 30-foot long tail.

Size:
Length – 70 to 90 feet long
Height – 10 to 15 feet tall at the hips
Weight – 33 to 38 tons

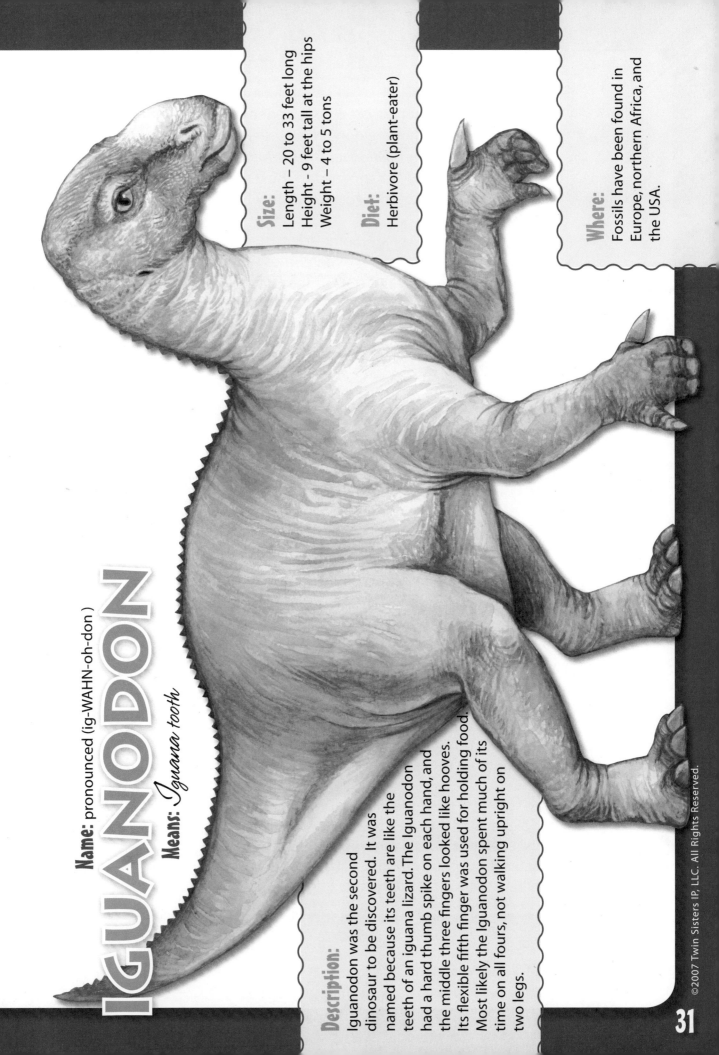

Name: pronounced (ig-WAHN-oh-don)

Means: *Iguana tooth*

IGUANODON

Description:

Iguanodon was the second dinosaur to be discovered. It was named because its teeth are like the teeth of an iguana lizard. The Iguanodon had a hard thumb spike on each hand, and the middle three fingers looked like hooves. Its flexible fifth finger was used for holding food. Most likely the Iguanodon spent much of its time on all fours, not walking upright on two legs.

Size:

Length – 20 to 33 feet long
Height - 9 feet tall at the hips
Weight – 4 to 5 tons

Diet:

Herbivore (plant-eater)

Where:

Fossils have been found in Europe, northern Africa, and the USA.

Theories?

The dinosaurs mysteriously went **extinct** (ex-stink-t) which means they are gone forever. Paleontologists and other scientists have several **theories**, or ideas, about what happened to the dinosaurs. So, what caused the dinosaurs to die out? No one knows for sure.

Some scientists think that a meteorite—a rock from outerspace— may have slammed into the earth. The meteorite may have been larger than Mount Everest.

After hitting the earth, much of the earth was on fire and the air was filled with thick smoke and dust. The sun was completely blocked out and soon all the plants stopped growing. The dinosaurs and other animals then died because there was nothing for them to eat.

Other scientists think the dinosaurs died of excessive heat when the earth's climate became warmer. Still others believe the dinosaurs died of starvation because the earth's climate got too cold for plants to grow.

Paleontologists

Scientists called **paleontologists** (pay-lee-on-tall-oh-gists) study fossils. The paleontologists listed below have made significant discoveries. Choose a paleontologist and search for that scientist's name online or in reference books. Answer the following questions.

Where did the paleontologist work?
What did the paleontologist discover?
What dinosaurs has the paleontologist named?

Gideon Mantell (1790-1852)

Robert Bakker (1945 -)

Mary Anning (1799-1847)

James I. Kirkland (1954 -)

Othniel Marsh (1831-1899)

Paul C. Sereno (1958 -)

Edward Drinker Cope (1840-1897)

Don Lessem (1951 -)

Roy C. Andrews (1884-1960)

Sue Hendrickson (1949 -)

Roland T. Bird (1899-1978)

The Paleontologists' Tools

Paleontologists use many tools when digging for fossils. Unscramble the letters to learn what tools you should bring on a dinosaur dig.

gifynganim sglsa
to examine small fossils

_____

aaermc
take photographs of the site and the fossils

_____

ptae sumaere
to measure the size of the bones

_____

kteobono
to keep a record of where you search and what you find

_____

ramemh dna lisehc
to carefully chip away the rock

_____

surbh
to lightly brush away the dirt around the fossil

_____

The Paleontologists' Tools

Now that you've decided where to search and have collected the tools, you're ready to dig!

First, **paleontologists walk through the site looking for any clues that dinosaur bones are below**. Sometimes the scientist will find very small bone chips. This might be a good place to dig!

Next, **paleontologists may use a hammer and chisel to carefully chip away any rock covering the top of the fossil**. Before removing the fossil paleontologists will **draw a very detailed map of the site** and take many photographs. The map and photographs show exactly where each fossil was found.

Finally, the **paleontologists will work together to remove the fossil.** To protect the fossil, team members wrap it in newspaper, foil, or cloth.

The fossil is taken to a laboratory. The goal is to remove the fossil bone or fragment from the rock. Team members clean the fossil by brushing, chipping, or even blasting away any dirt or rock. They must be very careful not to damage the fossil.

Paleontologists try to identify the dinosaur by studying the bones and fragments. Team members may preserve the fossil with special glues or plastics, and broken bones may be glued together.

The paleontologists try to put the bones together—just like a giant puzzle. Because many bones may be missing, paleontologists must look at other dinosaur fossils.

Map Out The Site

Imagine your backyard or a favorite park is the site of a dinosaur dig. Remember, before removing the fossils paleontologists will draw a very detailed map of the site and take many photographs.

Draw a very detailed map of your dinosaur dig below. Show where the dinosaur bones are found!

Design Your Own Dinosaur!

Start with the doodle below and create a dinosaur! Add a head and legs! Will your dinosaur have a long or short tail? Spikes or horns? Scales or feathers?

Prehistoric Dig

Find each of the dinosaurs and prehistoric reptiles below. Search horizontally, vertically or diagonally.

Stegosaurus
Giganotosaurus
Saltopus
Tyrannosaurus rex

Plesiosaurus
Pteranodon
Brachiosaurus
Ichthyosaurus

Triceratops
Allosaurus
Compsognathus
Quetzalcoatlus

O E S I O O H A L L O S A U N A D I O N
U O O P L E S I O S A U R U S E S A P L
A L T B E C O M P S O G N A T H U S T I
X U T Y R A N N O S A U R U S R E X E A
B P G U R S G O A S S S O T N N S U R R
R I T I I A I I S L S L R A U T S R A U
A C A S G R N I G G L U R A O U T S N U
C H T U A A A N T A A O S U L S E A O U
H T S Z Q U N G O S N O S T E T G L T C
I H T A H S O O O S I O A A N A O T R T
O Y R U L L N I T H A O T U U I S O A U
S O I S N T S C C O C U R O T R A G T U
A S C S O E O A H L S U R P S U U C R R
U A E R L H R P A A A M U P A R S N A
R U R P S B N Z U S G E U O S U U O D O
U I A Q H U T U O S D U G R P A S R S R
S A T U B E U G P T E R A N O D O N U L
S O O O U P E T R I C E R A T B R C M S
A S P Q I T I C H T H Y O S A U R U S B
U O S A S U R O H O O U N U U T O S R R H U

Coffee Ground Fossils

Make your own prehistoric fossils overnight!

What you will need:

- 1 cup of used coffee grounds
- 1/2 cup of cold coffee
- 1 cup of flour
- 1/2 cup of salt
- Waxed paper
- Mixing bowl

- Small objects to make impressions in the dough
- Empty can or a butter knife
- Toothpicks (optional)
- String to hang your fossil (optional)

Mix together the coffee grounds, cold coffee, flour, and salt. Knead the dough and then flatten it out onto the waxed paper. Cut out circles of the dough with a can. Or, use the dull knife to cut pieces large enough to fit your "fossil" objects. Press your objects firmly into the dough. When you take the object out, you will have your fossil impression. If you want to hang the fossil, poke a hole through the circle near the edge. Poke the string through the hole and tie together the ends. Let the fossil dry overnight and then hang it for everybody to see!

Possible Fossil Objects

- **Small plastic dinosaurs**
- **Dog biscuits**
- **Leftover chicken bones**
- **Shells from peanuts, walnuts**
- **Coins**

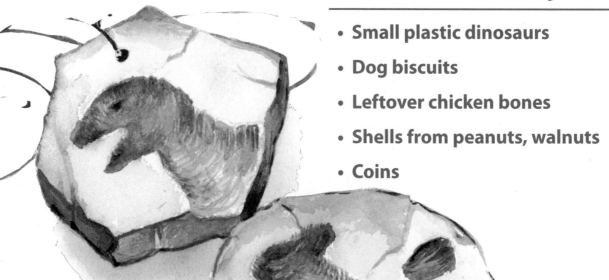

Homemade Dinosaur Bones

Make your own dinosaur bones at home!

What you will need:

- Large cardboard tube
  (a gift wrap tube or a paper towel tube)
- Large plastic bowl
- Stirrer (to mix the flour glue)
- Flour
- Water
- Newspaper or brown paper bags
- Masking tape
- White, yellow or tan tempera paint
- Brush

Before you begin, ask an adult to make simple thin glue from flour and water. Mix 1 cup of flour into 1 cup of water until the mixture is thin and runny. Stir it into 4 cups of boiling water. Simmer for about 3 minutes and then cool.

Crumble newspaper into two balls. Tape a ball to each end of the cardboard tube. Tear strips of newspaper and/or brown bag paper. You'll need a lot of strips! Dip a newspaper strip into the cooled glue and then wrap it around the dinosaur bone. Cover the ends and the tube—the entire bone. Allow the bone to dry completely and then paint it!

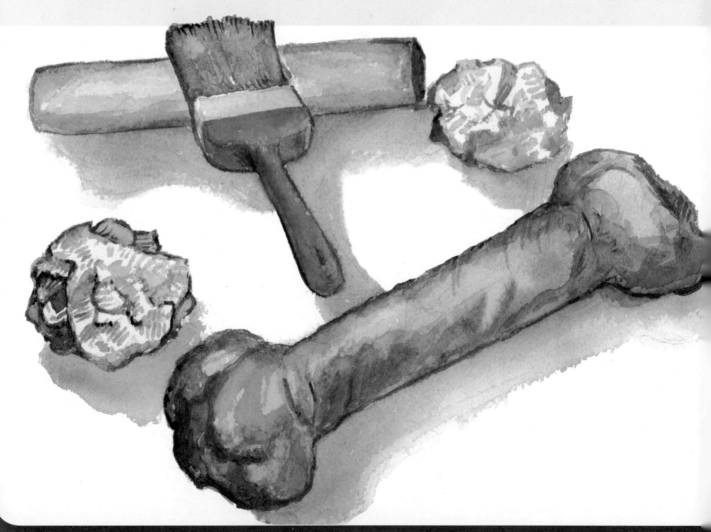

Dinosaur Feet

You'll need two empty tissue boxes that are the same size. Cut and glue in place a piece of cardboard or posterboard that fits inside the openings of each box. This will make them smaller so your feet will stay inside of them. Paint the boxes and allow them to dry, or you can also cover the boxes with construction paper. Remember, no one knows the colors of the dinosaurs! Make toenails by cutting out triangles from construction paper or craft foam. Glue them in place. Once the glue has dried, try on your new dinosaur feet!

Dinosaur Eggs

Before you begin, ask an adult to make simple thin glue from flour and water. Mix 1 cup of flour into 1 cup of water until the mixture is thin and runny. Stir it into 4 cups of boiling water. Simmer for about 3 minutes and then cool.

Blow up a large balloon. Tear strips of newspaper and/or brown paper bag. You'll need a lot of strips! Dip a newspaper strip into the cooled glue and then wrap it around the balloon. Let the dinosaur egg dry for a few days. When the egg is dry, you can pop the balloon and remove it from inside the egg. Decorate the egg with paint or markers. Remember that no one knows the color of the dinosaurs' eggs!

Gridlock

Solve each riddle by reading the grid coordinates and filling in the letters on the blanks below. The first number in the coordinate tells you how many columns over the letter will be. (Follow the blue numbers below the grid.) The second number tells you how many rows up the letter will be. (Follow the green numbers that go up the side of the grid.)

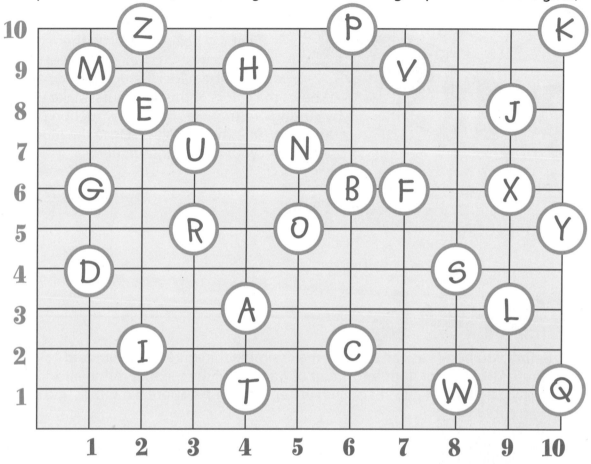

1. What do you call a Triceratops that fell down the stairs?

$\dfrac{}{}$

$\dfrac{}{1:4} \dfrac{}{2:2} \dfrac{}{5:7} \dfrac{}{5:5} \qquad \dfrac{}{8:4} \dfrac{}{4:3} \dfrac{}{3:7} \dfrac{}{3:5}$

2. How long should a dinosaur's legs be?

$\dfrac{}{9:3} \dfrac{}{5:5} \dfrac{}{5:7} \dfrac{}{1:6} \qquad \dfrac{}{2:8} \dfrac{}{5:7} \dfrac{}{5:5} \dfrac{}{3:7} \dfrac{}{1:6} \dfrac{}{4:9} \qquad \dfrac{}{4:1} \dfrac{}{5:5}$

$\dfrac{}{3:3} \dfrac{}{2:8} \dfrac{}{4:3} \dfrac{}{6:2} \dfrac{}{4:9} \qquad \dfrac{}{4:1} \dfrac{}{4:9} \dfrac{}{2:8} \qquad \dfrac{}{1:6} \dfrac{}{3:5} \dfrac{}{5:5} \dfrac{}{3:7} \dfrac{}{5:7} \dfrac{}{1:4}$

3. What do you call a scared Tyrannosaurus rex?

$\dfrac{}{4:3} \qquad \dfrac{}{5:7} \dfrac{}{2:8} \dfrac{}{3:5} \dfrac{}{7:9} \dfrac{}{5:5} \dfrac{}{3:7} \dfrac{}{8:4} \qquad \dfrac{}{3:5} \dfrac{}{2:8} \dfrac{}{9:6}$

4. What do you get when you cross a dinosaur with a lemon?

$$\underline{}$$

$\overline{4:3}$ $\overline{1:4}$ $\overline{2:2}$ $\overline{5:7}$ $\overline{5:5}$ $\overline{8:4}$ $\overline{5:5}$ $\overline{3:7}$ $\overline{3:5}$

5. What was Tyrannosaurus rex's favorite number?

$\overline{2:8}$ $\overline{2:2}$ $\overline{1:6}$ $\overline{4:9}$ $\overline{4:1}$ ($\overline{4:3}$ $\overline{4:1}$ $\overline{2:8}$)

6. What do you get when you cross a dinosaur with fireworks?

$\overline{1:4}$ $\overline{2:2}$ $\overline{5:7}$ $\overline{5:5}$ $\overline{1:9}$ $\overline{2:2}$ $\overline{4:1}$ $\overline{2:8}$

7. What do you get if you cross a Triceratops with a kangaroo?

$\overline{4:1}$ $\overline{3:5}$ $\overline{2:2}$ $\overline{6:2}$ $\overline{2:8}$ $\overline{3:5}$ $\overline{4:3}$ $\overline{4:9}$ $\overline{5:5}$ $\overline{6:10}$ $\overline{8:4}$

8. What did dinosaurs have that no other animals ever had?

$\overline{6:6}$ $\overline{4:3}$ $\overline{6:6}$ $\overline{10:5}$ $\overline{1:4}$ $\overline{2:2}$ $\overline{5:7}$ $\overline{5:5}$ $\overline{8:4}$ $\overline{4:3}$ $\overline{3:7}$ $\overline{3:5}$ $\overline{8:4}$

9. What makes more noise than a dinosaur?

$\overline{4:1}$ $\overline{8:1}$ $\overline{5:5}$ $\overline{1:4}$ $\overline{2:2}$ $\overline{5:7}$ $\overline{5:5}$ $\overline{8:4}$ $\overline{4:3}$ $\overline{3:7}$ $\overline{3:5}$ $\overline{8:4}$

10. What do you call a dinosaur that left its armor out in the rain?

$\overline{4:3}$ $\overline{8:4}$ $\overline{4:1}$ $\overline{2:8}$ $\overline{1:6}$ $\overline{5:5}$ $\overline{8:4}$ $\overline{4:3}$ $\overline{3:7}$ $\overline{3:5}$ $\overline{3:7}$ $\overline{8:4}$ $\overline{4:1}$

Name Those Prehistoric Reptiles

1 _____

2 _____

3 _____

4 _____

5 _____

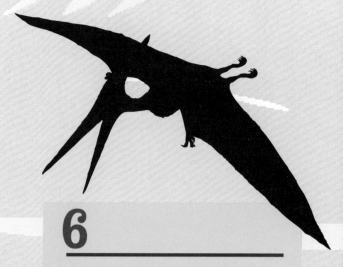

6 _____

Name Those Prehistoric Reptiles

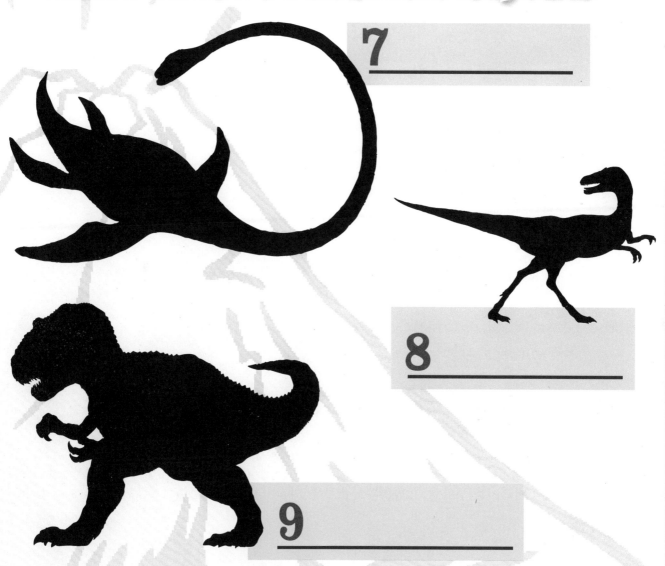

7 _____

8 _____

9 _____

10 _____

11 _____

Backyard Dinosaur Dig

Count out a quantity of bone-shaped dog treats. Scatter the "dinosaur" bones in a small area of the yard. Pour dry, clean sand over the bones. Give each player a small paint brush. Players carefully brush away the sand searching for bones. Continue until all the bones are discovered.

Option: Purchase a dinosaur craft kit from a hobby or toy store. Hide the pieces in the sand. Assemble the dinosaur when all or most of the bones have been discovered.

Prehistoric Window Clings

Use these instructions to make your own clings.

You will need
- *Regular white paper glue*
- *Food coloring of your choice*
- *Clear film (transparency sheets work well)*
- *Patterns*

Mix a few drops of food coloring to the white glue bottle and mix well. Put your design under the clear film and trace over it with a continuous bead of glue and fill in. Let dry for at least 12 hours. Peel your work of art off of the film and place on any glass surface.

Dinosaur Soaps

You will need:
- *Clear glycerin soap*
- *Colored glycerin soap*
- *Soap molds or plastic ice cube trays*
- *Plastic dinosaurs*

- *Microwave*
- *Glass measuring cups*
- *Sharp knife*
- *Optional: glitter and fragrance oil*

1. Have an adult cut colored glycerin soap into 1/4" cubes.

2. Have an adult cut clear glycerin soap into 1" cubes. Place the cubes into glass measuring cups and melt the cubes in the microwave on high for 15 seconds at a time. Check between times. Do not overheat the soap; just melt it.

3. Place small plastic dinosaurs into the molds. Pour the melted clear glycerin over the dinosaurs.

4. Carefully place small colored pieces of glycerin into the mold around the dinosaur.

5. Allow the soaps to cool 1 to 2 hours, or place them into a refrigerator for 30 minutes.

6. Lightly twist the mold and remove soaps. Soaps can be placed in a clear cellophane bag and decorated with stickers for gift giving.

Dinosaur Name Game

Dinosaurs are named using the Latin and Greek languages. The words or syllables often describe the unique features or characteristics of the dinosaur. For example, the longest dinosaur name belongs to one of the smallest dinosaurs: *Micropachycephalosaurus.* Use the chart below to describe this dinosaur.

name	meaning	name	meaning
ALLO	STRANGE	MEGA	LARGE
ANKYLO	CROOKED	MICRO	SMALL
ANURO	NO TAIL	NODO	LUMPY
APATO	DECEPTIVE	ORNITHO	BIRD
BARY	HEAVY	PACHY	THICK
BRACHIO	ARM	POD	FOOT
CEPHALO	HEAD	RAPTOR	ROBBER
CEROS	HORN	REX	KING
COMPSO	PRETTY	SAUR(AS)	LIZARD
DACTYL	EYE	STEGO	ROOF
DI	TWO	TRI	THREE
DINO	TERRIBLE	TYRRANNO	TYRANT
MASSO	HEAVY	VELOCI	SPEEDY

Use this chart to create new names for imaginary dinosaurs or real friends! For example, if your new dinosaur is a small, without a tail, and has two eyes its name might be *microdidactyl.*

Velociceros

_____   _____

_____   _____

_____   _____

_____   _____

_____   _____

_____   _____

Codebreaker Dinosaur Jokes

Use the symbol coded letters to solve the riddles.

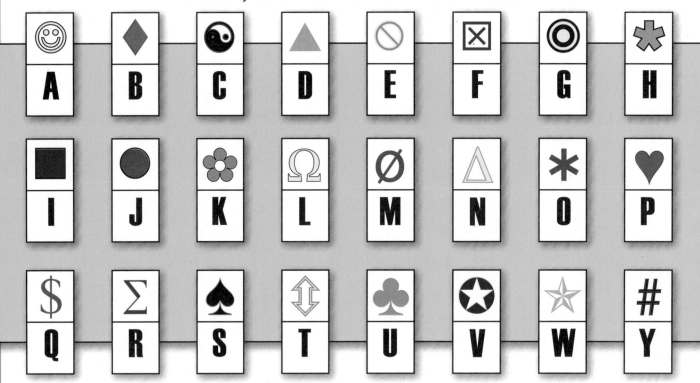

What do you get when a dinosaur sneezes?

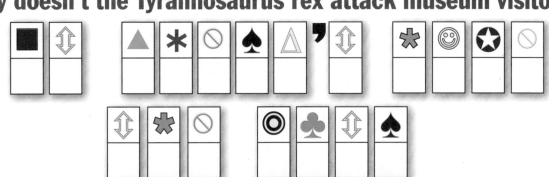

Where did Velociraptor buy things?

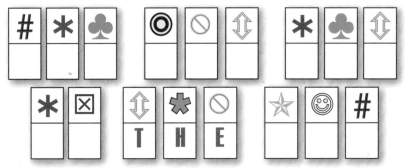

Why doesn't the Tyrannosaurus rex attack museum visitors?

Codebreaker Dinosaur Jokes

Why did Apatosaurus devour the factory?

What do you call 100 dinosaurs dancing?

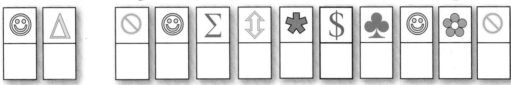

What is as big as the biggest dinosaur but weighs nothing?

What do you call a sleeping Brachiosaurus?

What does T. Rex use to travel from planet to planet?

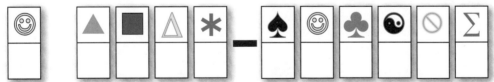

What should you do if you find a dinosaur sleeping in your bed?

Paleontology Puzzle

1. Cut out the puzzle on pages 51 and 53. Keep the pieces for each dinosaur separate.

2. Mix up the pieces of one dinosaur. Time yourself to see how quickly you can put the dinosaur puzzle together. Record your time in the chart.

Name	Time to make the first dinosaur		Time to make the second dinosaur		Add the times		Time with both dinosaurs mixed up	
	min.	sec.	min.	sec.	min.	sec.	min.	sec.

3. Mix up the pieces of the second dinosaur. Time yourself to see how quickly you can put that dinosaur puzzle together. Record your time in the chart.

4. Add the times for the two dinosaurs to see how long it takes to make both dinosaurs.

5. Do you think it will take you more or less time to put together the dinosaurs if the pieces from both puzzles were mixed together?

6. Now test your prediction. Mix the pieces from both dinosaurs together. Time yourself to see how quickly you can put both dinosaur puzzles together. Record your time in the chart.

THINK ABOUT IT!

Did it take you longer to assemble the two dinosaurs when they were done one at a time or when they were mixed up together?

Would it be easier for a paleontologist to recreate a dinosaur if she or he found the bones from just one animal or if the bones of more than one animal were mixed together?

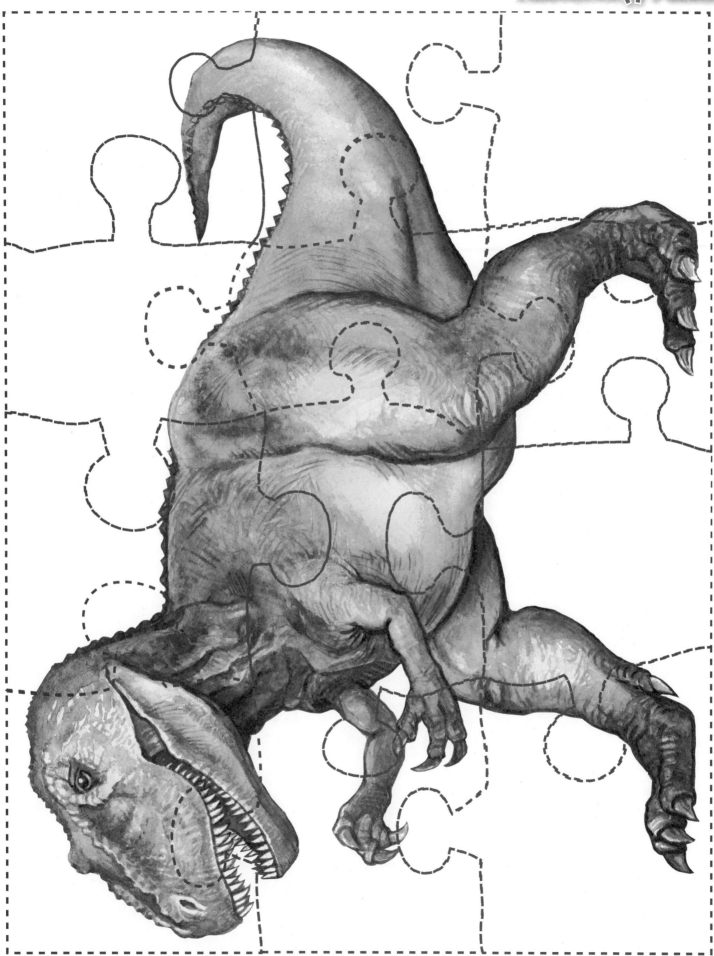

This page was intentionally left blank for the Paleontology Puzzle activity to be completed.

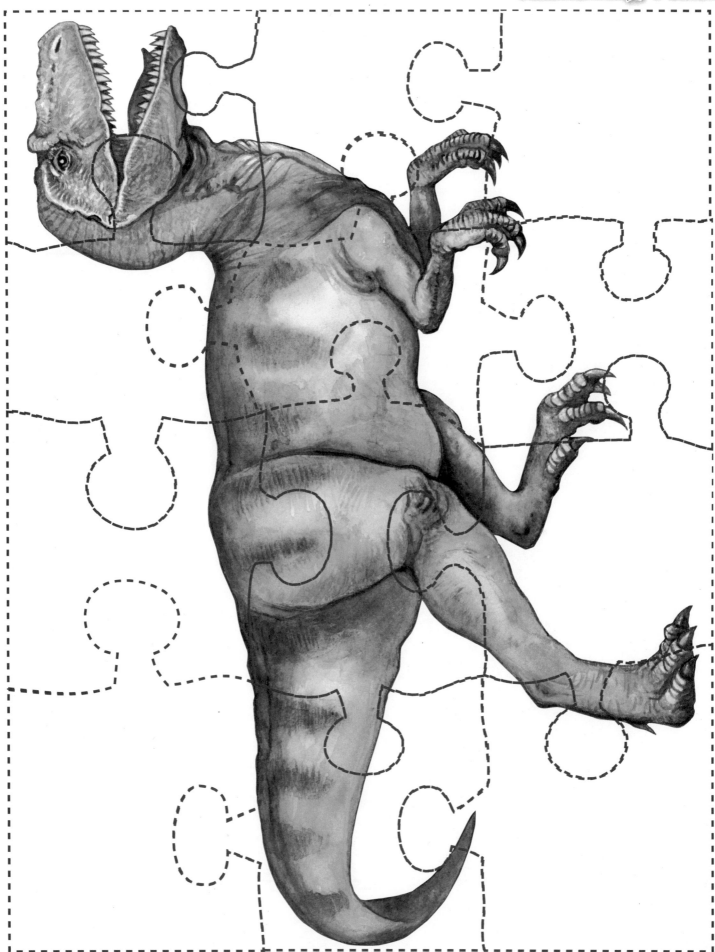

This page was intentionally left blank for the Paleontology Puzzle activity to be completed.

Dino Slapstick Story

Ask a friend to give you a word for each clue below. Then read the story using your friend's words.

Dear 1) _____,

Last week, my friend and I met a real, live dinosaur. At first it looked like a 2) _____, but then I heard it 3) _____. I knew then that it was a 4) _____. I was 5) _____ and started to run. But my friend, 6) _____, who knew a lot about dinosaurs, said the dinosaur was 7) _____. It had escaped from 8) _____. She told me not to be afraid because the dinosaur would eat only 9) _____, not people. I reached out to gently pet the dinosaur. Its skin was 10) _____ and 11) _____. The dinosaur smiled. We decided to hide the dinosaur in 12) _____. My friend 13) _____ in front of the dinosaur while I 14) _____ in back of the dinosaur, but the dinosaur wouldn't move. Soon, a crowd of people gathered around the dinosaur. Some people were 15) _____ and others were 16) _____. The dinosaur just 17) _____. The crowd of people slowly led the dinosaur to 18) _____. When you come to visit, I'll introduce you to the dinosaur. His name is 19) _____.

Love,

20) _____

1) A friend's name _____

2) Large object _____

3) Sound _____

4) Type of Dinosaur _____

5) Feeling _____

6) A friend's name _____

7) Adjective _____

8) Place _____

9) Food _____

10) Adjective _____

11) Adjective _____

12) Place _____

13) Past tense verb _____

14) Past tense verb _____

15) Feeling _____

16) Verb ending in –ing _____

17) Past tense verb _____

18) Place _____

19) Name _____

20) Your name _____

Dinosaur Construction

Plot the coordinates below. Connect them like dot to dot as you go.

① (2, 2)
② (4, 1)
③ (6, 2)
④ (6, 5)
⑤ (7, 4)
⑥ (7, 2)
⑦ (6, 1)
⑧ (8, 1)
⑨ (9, 2)
⑩ (9, 4)
⑪ (11, 3)
⑫ (12, 3)
⑬ (13, 2)

⑭ (12, 1)
⑮ (14, 1)
⑯ (14, 2)
⑰ (15, 1)
⑱ (16, 1)
⑲ (16, 2)
⑳ (15, 3)
㉑ (16, 4)
㉒ (18, 3)
㉓ (20, 2)
㉔ (23, 1)
㉕ (28, 2)

㉖ (22, 2)
㉗ (21, 3)
㉘ (19, 5)
㉙ (17, 7)
㉚ (14, 9)
㉛ (11, 10)
㉜ (7, 10)
㉝ (6, 11)
㉞ (5, 12)
㉟ (6, 15)
㊱ (6, 16)
㊲ (5, 18)

㊳ (4, 19)
㊴ (3, 19)
㊵ (1, 18)
㊶ (2, 17)
㊷ (4, 17)
㊸ (4, 14)
㊹ (3, 11)
㊺ (2, 8)
㊻ (3, 7)
㊼ (4, 6)
㊽ (4, 4)
㊾ (3, 3)
㊿ (2, 2)

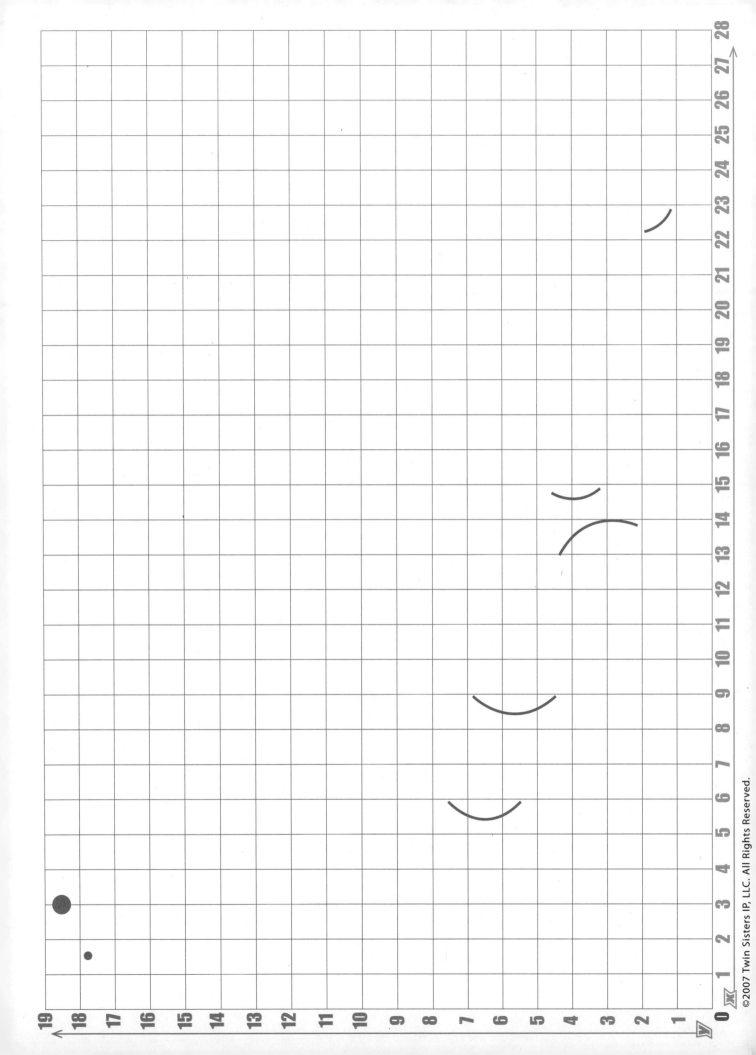

Life-size T. Rex Head

Create a life-size drawing of the head of a Tyrannosaurus rex.

Use a 3 x 4 foot piece of paper. Using a pencil and a ruler, carefully measure and lightly draw 6 x 6-inch squares. Your paper will have 6 columns and 8 rows. Now, draw each square from the grid below on your large paper. Be sure to match the grid exactly.

Option: Work together with others to create the life-size drawing of Tyrannosaurus rex. Cut out 48 6 x 6-inch squares of white paper. Number each square. Players draw the corresponding square from the grid below. Tape the completed grids to a wall in the correct order.

In The Footsteps of T. Rex

Make two Tyrannosaurus rex footprints. Use the grid below as a guide to draw the Tyrannosaurus footprint onto a large piece of paper. Draw a second footprint on another large piece of paper. Each square is 12-inches. Each Tyrannosaurus rex footprint should measure about 36-inches long and 24-inches wide.

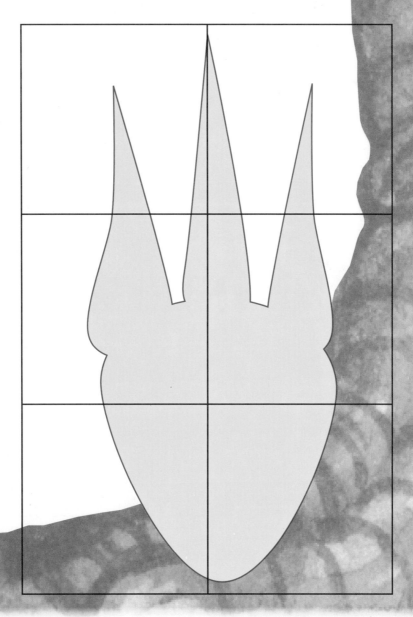

Take the Tyrannosaurus rex footprints outside. Imagine a T-rex walking through your neighborhood. Lay one footprint on the sidewalk. Take 12 to 15 giant steps and lay the second footprint on the sidewalk. If T-rex was walking quickly through your neighborhood, the footprints would be about 20 feet apart!

Crossword Puzzles

Complete the crossword puzzle. If you need help, use the Word Bank.

2. had a frill that may have protected my neck and shoulders.

5. was huge but my arms were only about 3 feet long and my hands had two fingers.

6. had spikes at the end of my flexible tail.

Word Bank

Tyrannosaurus rex
Triceratops
Plesiosaurus
Brachiosaurus
Stegosaurus
Quetzalcoatlus

DOWN

1. was the largest flying animal ever found.

3. had four paddle-like legs similar to those of a marine turtle.

4. weighed about the same as 20 large elephants

Crossword Puzzles

Complete the crossword puzzle. If you need help, use the Word Bank.

ACROSS

3. I had four crescent-shaped fins, a dorsal fin, and a fish-like tail.

4. I was named for my unusual backbone; my vertebrae was lighter than those of other dinosaurs.

5. I was a small dinosaur that walked on two legs, had hollow bones, and a long head with dozens of small, sharp teeth.

6. My wing-span was longer than that of any known bird.

Word Bank

Compsognathus
Giganotosaurus
Pteranodon
Saltopus
Allosaurus
Ichthyosaurus

DOWN

1. I was about the size of a chicken.

2. I was longer than T. Rex and had a 6-foot long skull

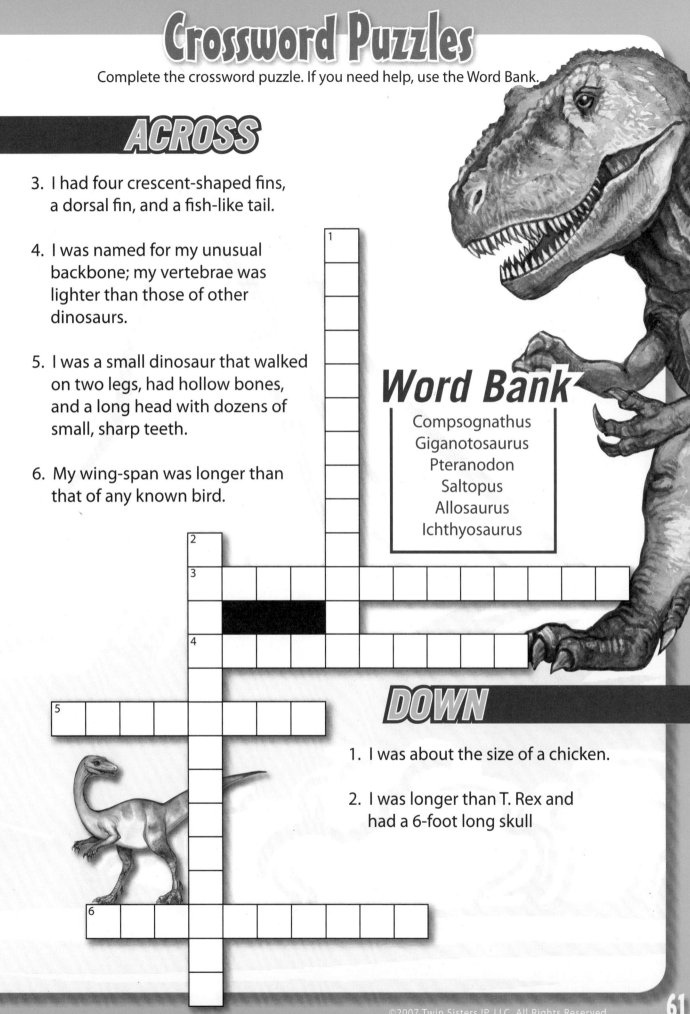

Dinosaur Construction

Plot the coordinates below. Connect them like dot to dot as you go.

① (8, 4)
② (9, 3)
③ (10, 2)
④ (10, 3)
⑤ (11, 2)
⑥ (11, 3)
⑦ (14, 2)
⑧ (12, 4)
⑨ (13, 6)
⑩ (15, 6)
⑪ (16, 2)
⑫ (19, 2)
⑬ (17, 3)
⑭ (17, 5)
⑮ (19, 3)

⑯ (20, 2)
⑰ (22, 2)
⑱ (20, 3)
⑲ (20, 5)
⑳ (22, 5)
㉑ (23, 5)
㉒ (25, 5)
㉓ (26, 6)
㉔ (25, 7)
㉕ (24, 8)
㉖ (23, 9)
㉗ (23, 8)
㉘ (22, 8)
㉙ (22, 10)
㉚ (21, 9)

㉛ (20, 10)
㉜ (20, 11)
㉝ (19, 11)
㉞ (18, 12)
㉟ (17, 13)
㊱ (17, 11)
㊲ (16, 13)
㊳ (15, 12)
㊴ (11, 12)
㊵ (9, 11)
㊶ (8, 11)
㊷ (7, 10)
㊸ (5, 9)
㊹ (4, 10)
㊺ (4, 12)

㊻ (6, 14)
㊼ (7, 14)
㊽ (8, 15)
㊾ (8, 16)
㊿ (6, 16)
51 (5, 15)
52 (5, 14)
53 (3, 13)
54 (2, 12)
55 (2, 10)
56 (4, 8)
57 (6, 7)
58 (9, 7)
59 (10, 6)
60 (8, 4)

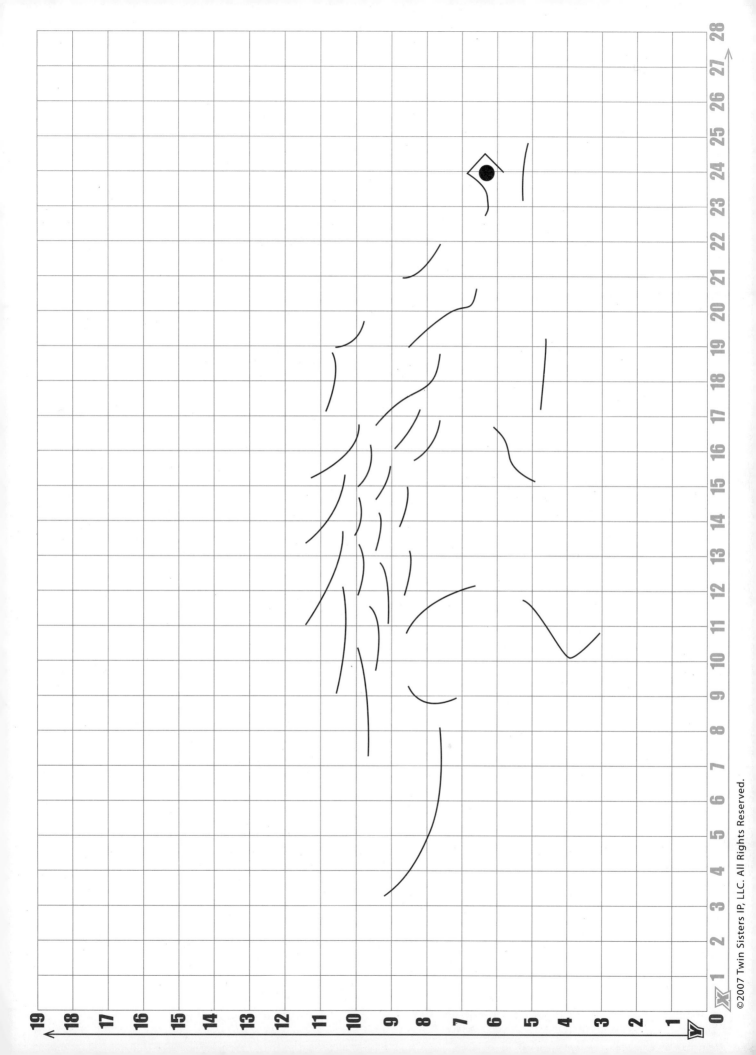

My Pet Dinosaur

My pet dinosaur is a _____

_____

Its name is _____

During the day my pet dinosaur _____

_____

_____

_____

At night my pet dinosaur _____

_____

_____

_____

_____

My pet dinosaur eats _____

_____

_____

_____

_____

My pet dinosaur and I like to _____

_____

_____

_____

64

Dino Match Up

Cut out the pieces below along the dotted lines and then turn them over to the blank side and mix them up. Try to find each dinosaur's match!

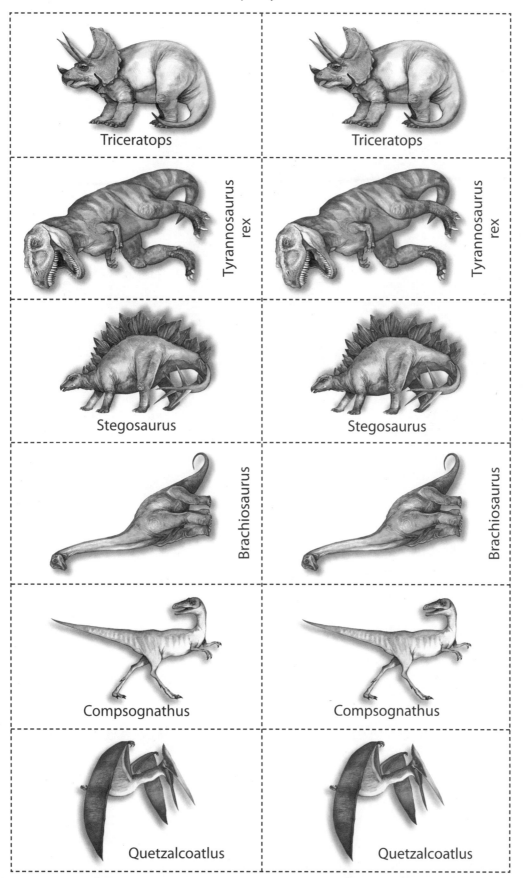

Triceratops   Triceratops

Tyrannosaurus rex   Tyrannosaurus rex

Stegosaurus   Stegosaurus

Brachiosaurus   Brachiosaurus

Compsognathus   Compsognathus

Quetzalcoatlus   Quetzalcoatlus

This page was intentionally left blank for the
Dino Match Up activity to be completed.

Dino Match Up

Cut out the pieces below along the dotted lines and then turn them over to the blank side and mix them up. Try to find each dinosaur's match!

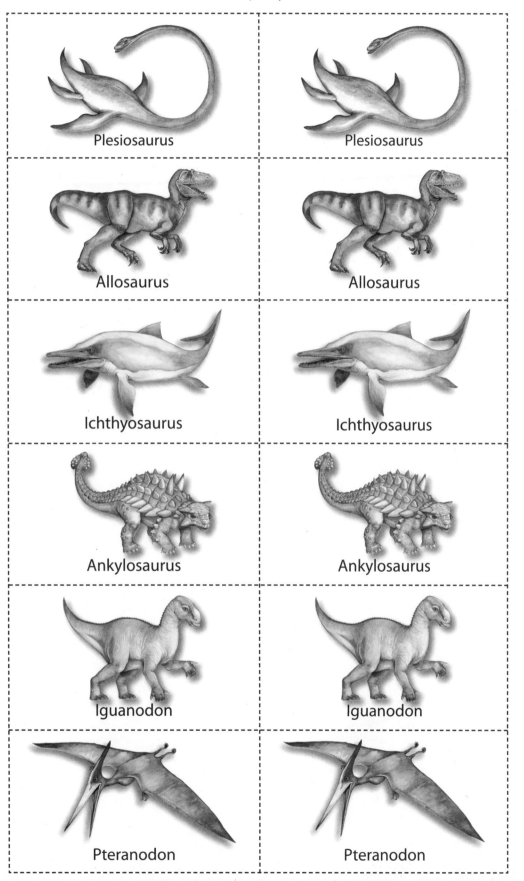

Plesiosaurus

Plesiosaurus

Allosaurus

Allosaurus

Ichthyosaurus

Ichthyosaurus

Ankylosaurus

Ankylosaurus

Iguanodon

Iguanodon

Pteranodon

Pteranodon

This page was intentionally left blank for the
Dino Match Up activity to be completed.

Dino-MAZE-ing

Help the Saltopus find its eggs by
guiding it through the maze.

My Life As A Dinosaur

Pretend that you could become a real, living dinosaur. Answer the following questions.

What dinosaur would you like to be? Why?

_____

_____

_____

_____

Where in the world would you want to live?

_____

_____

_____

_____

Would you rather be a prehistoric herbivore or carnivore? Why?

_____

_____

_____

_____

Would you make grunts, snorts, hoots, squeaks, honks, or some other sound?

_____

_____

_____

_____

What would you do all day?

_____

_____

_____

_____

What would you add to your body so you could defend yourself against predators? Why?

_____

_____

_____

Dinosaur Construction

Plot the coordinates below. Connect them like dot to dot as you go.

1. (5, 1)
2. (9, 2)
3. (11, 2)
4. (10, 3)
5. (11, 4)
6. (11, 6)
7. (12, 7)
8. (14, 6)
9. (15, 6)
10. (16, 4)
11. (19, 3)
12. (20, 2)
13. (18, 1)
14. (20, 1)
15. (21, 0)
16. (21, 1)
17. (23, 1)
18. (22, 2)
19. (21, 2)
20. (21, 4)
21. (20, 5)
22. (19, 5)
23. (20, 6)
24. (23, 6)
25. (25, 7)
26. (27, 7)
27. (26, 10)
28. (25, 11)
29. (27, 12)
30. (25, 12)
31. (24, 11)
32. (24, 10)
33. (25, 9)
34. (25, 8)
35. (22, 9)
36. (19, 10)
37. (16, 12)
38. (14, 13)
39. (12, 13)
40. (11, 14)
41. (10, 14)
42. (10, 16)
43. (9, 18)
44. (7, 18)
45. (6, 17)
46. (4, 17)
47. (3, 16)
48. (9, 16)
49. (6, 15)
50. (4, 15)
51. (5, 14)
52. (7, 14)
53. (7, 13)
54. (8, 13)
55. (8, 12)
56. (7, 12)
57. (6, 11)
58. (7, 10)
59. (7, 11)
60. (8, 11)
61. (8, 10)
62. (9, 10)
63. (9, 11)
64. (10, 9)
65. (8, 8)
66. (8, 4)
67. (7, 3)
68. (5, 2)
69. (6, 2)
70. (5, 1)

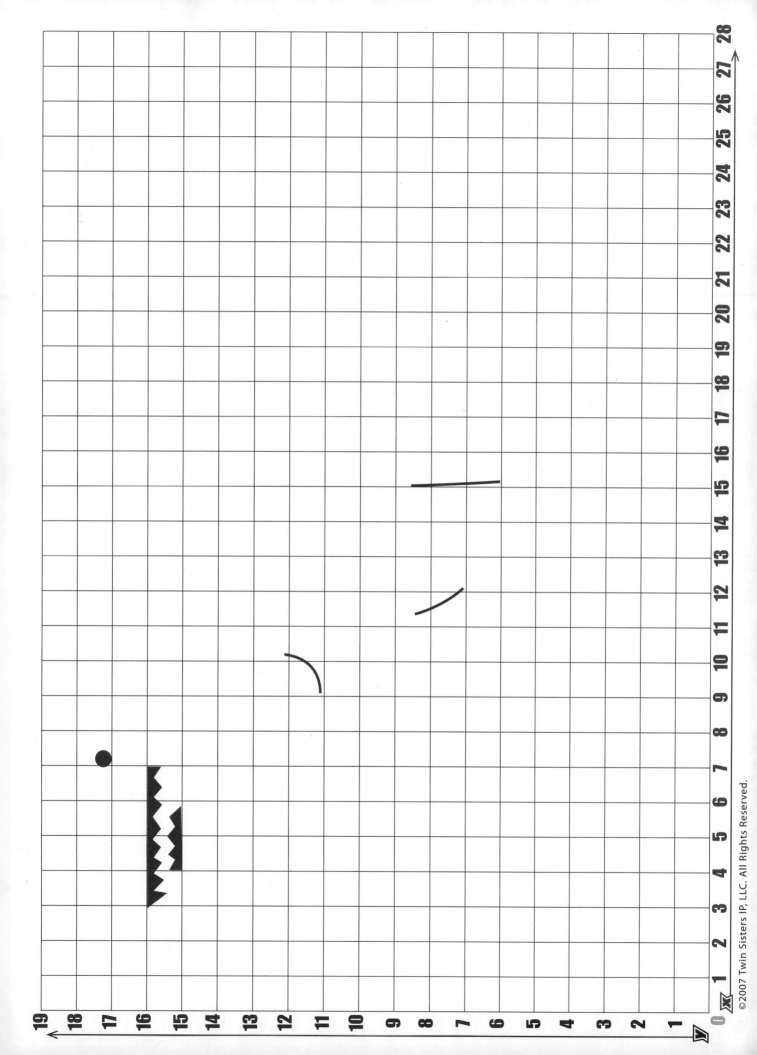

New Discoveries!

Plateosaurus, the world's deepest dinosaur find

Plateosaurus fossils were discovered over 7,000 feet below the North Sea in Norway. Paleontologists believe Plateosaurus may have been up to 30 feet long and weighed up to four tons.

Bigger Than T. rex and Giganotosaurus!

Meat-eating dinosaurs larger than Tyrannosaurus rex and Giganotosaurus have been discovered in Argentina. Paleontologists named the new species of dinosaur *mapusaurus roseae*. Seven of the dinosaurs were discovered together in one location.

Mini-Sauropods

Paleontologists discovered the fossil remains of 11 miniature sauropods in Germany. Sauropods, like Brachiosaurus, were the largest of all the dinosaurs. But these miniature sauropds are only from 5 to 20 feet long. Paleontologists first thought the dinosaurs were young sauropods. But now they believe the dinosaurs were miniature or dwarf sauropods.

My, what a long neck you have

Paleontologists found a sauropod with one of the longest necks and smallest bodies. The individual bones in the neck are each nearly 2 feet long. Paleontologists estimate the neck of Erketu ellisoni was about 24 feet long. But its body was only half as long as its neck. Paleontologists also think that it may have walked with its neck parallel to the ground—not up high like other sauropods.

A Turkey Dinosaur?

Imagine a 7-foot tall turkey dinosaur? Paleontologists discovered the fossil remains of *Hagryphus giganteus* in Utah. The dinosaur had a strong toothless beak, powerful arms and long claws. Large feathers grew on the back end of the dinosaur after it lost its tail. This made the dinosaur look like a turkey.

Alike & Different

Dinosaur 1   Dinosaur 2

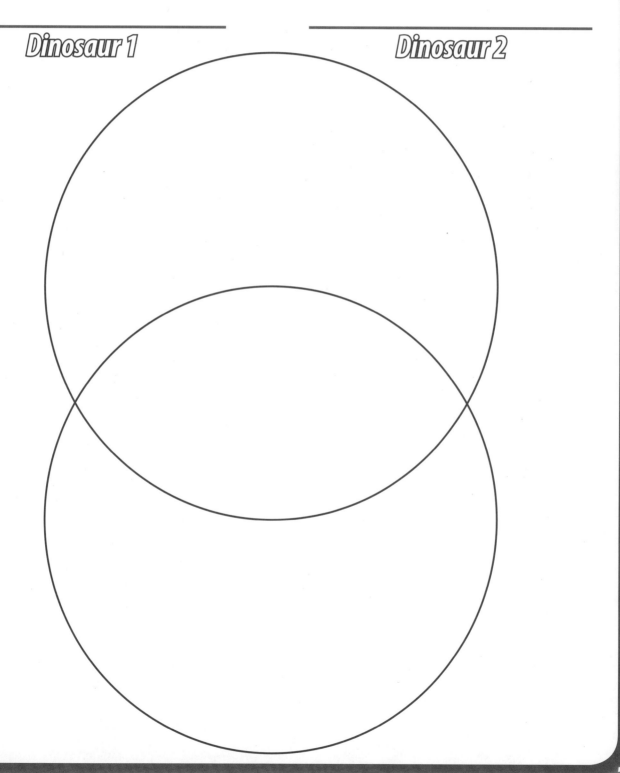

What Do You Feed A Hungry Dinosaur?

Paleontologists use clues from fossils to learn the kind of food different dinosaurs ate.

- Sharp, long, pointed teeth belonged to a carnivore.

- Short, flat fossil teeth belonged to an herbivore.

- Paleontologists have discovered fossils of dinosaur dung or droppings. If the dung contained seeds and leaves, it belonged to an herbivore. If the dung contained ground-up pieces of bone, it belonged to a carnivore.

- Paleontologists have discovered bones from another animal inside the fossil of a dinosaur. This means that the dinosaur must have been a carnivore.

- Many carnivores walked on their hind legs, had small arms, long, strong tails, and a mouth filled with very sharp teeth.

- Some carnivore dinosaurs are called **predators** because they hunted and killed smaller dinosaurs and animals.

- Other carnivore dinosaurs were **scavengers**; these dinosaurs would eat the leftovers of the predators.

- Most dinosaurs were herbivores; they ate small plants and bushes. Others were tall enough to eat leaves from the tops of tall trees.

- Many herbivores gobbled up plants without even chewing. Some would eat rocks to help digest the plants.

- Most plant-eaters walked on four legs. Many of the biggest dinosaurs called Sauropods were herbivores.

Who Ate What?

Circle the dinosaurs that were herbivores.
Draw an X through the dinosaurs
that were carnivores.
Use the clues
on page 76.

DINO-Cooking

Prehistoric Grub

¼ cup dirt—cocoa
½ cup swamp water—milk
2 cups crushed bones—sugar
½ cup fat—butter
2 cups grass—oatmeal
½ cup squashed bugs—peanut butter

Ask an adult to heat the first four ingredients to a boil. Add the grass. Remove from the mixture from the heat. Add the bugs. Drop the mixture by spoonfuls onto waxed paper. Allow to cool!

Pteranodon Wings

Served whole, chicken wings look similar to Pterandon wings. Wash and dry the wings. Hold onto wing tips and spread them so they look like they're flying. Dip each wing in barbecue sauce and place on foil-lined baking sheet. Bake for 20 to 25 minutes at 3750 F. Turn the wings carefully and bake for an additional 15 to 20 minutes. Make the Pteranodon wings ahead of time and reheat in a 200° F. oven for 15 to 20 minutes.

DINOSAUR TOENAILS

7 small corn or whole wheat tortillas
1 Tablespoon sugar
1/2 Tablespoon cinnamon

Preheat the oven to 450° F. Using clean scissors or a knife cut each tortilla into 6 wedges. Mix the cinnamon and sugar. Sprinkle the tortilla wedges with water and sprinkle with cinnamon-sugar. Place the dinosaur toenails on a cookie sheet and bake about 10 minutes, or until crisp.

DINO-Cooking

Fossil Soup

Dinosaur Bone – a meaty beef bone
8 carrots
6 celery stalks
4 potatoes - medium
2 large cans vegetable juice
2 tablespoons salt
6 cups water
2 bay leaves

Wash and cut the carrots, celery and potatoes. Combine the dinosaur bone, vegetable juice, and 6 cups of water. Add the salt and bay leaves. Cover and simmer for two hours. Add vegetables, cover and simmer one hour. Serve and enjoy.

DINOSAUR BONES

1 cup peanut butter
1 cup dry milk
2 Tablespoons honey
8 squares graham crackers
(finely crushed, set aside)

Combine the peanut butter and dry milk in a large bowl. Add the honey and mix well.

Divide the mixture into equal-size portions. Shape the mixture into dinosaur bones and sprinkle them with graham cracker crumbs.

Dinosaur Cake

Prepare your favorite 9 x 13" cake mix according to package directions.

1. Cut the cake like this:

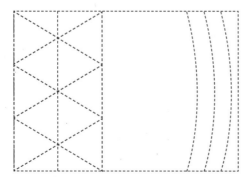

2. Arrange the pieces like this:

3. Frost the cake with any color frosting you prefer—no one knows the colors of the dinosaurs! Decorate the dinosaur cake with candy pieces, sprinkles, or cookies.

How much does it weigh?

Learn the estimated weight of a favorite dinosaur. Weigh yourself on a scale. Calculate how many of you it would take to weigh the same as the dinosaur.

The Longest Name

One of the smallest dinosaurs ever discovered has the longest name; *micropachycephalosaurus*. Its name means: tiny, thick-headed lizard. This dinosaur was only about 20 inches long!

MICROPACHYCEPHALOSAURUS

HOW TALL IS IT?

Learn the estimated length of one or more favorite dinosaurs. Use a measuring tape and chalk to mark the length and height of each dinosaur on a sidewalk or playground. Indoors, measure the length of the dinosaur with a ball of yarn. Ahead of time, tie knots in the yarn every five feet. Count by fives as the yarn is unrolled and stretched out to the length of the dinosaur. For more fun, have someone measure your height. Then calculate how many of you it would take to be the same length or height as your dinosaur.

Dinosaur Poetry

Write an acrostic poem by writing a sentence that begins with each letter in the word *dinosaur*. On another sheet of paper, write the name of your favorite dinosaur in a column, one letter on each line. Then write an acrostic poem about that dinosaur!

Find the Other Half

Twelve words below have been separated into two parts. Find the parts that fit together and write them in the answer area below. Cross off each part as you use it to make a word.

inct	carn	dino	pr
rep	ator	quad	ivore
paleon	prehi	tologist	fos
sil	ruped	pred	ey
storic	ext	ivore	tile
saur	herb	bi	ped

1. _____

2. _____

3. _____

4. _____

5. _____

6. _____

7. _____

8. _____

9. _____

10. _____

11. _____

12. _____

Dinosaur ABC's

Find a dinosaur whose name begins with each letter of the alphabet. Look through this book for the names of dinosaurs! Search online or in other books about dinosaurs to find other names.

A _____

B _____

C _____

D _____

E _____

F _____

G _____

H _____

I _____

J _____

K _____

L _____

M _____

N _____

O _____

P _____

Q _____

R _____

S _____

T _____

U _____

V _____

W _____

X _____

Y _____

Z _____

The DINO-graph

Graph the length of each dinosaur. Color all or part of a square to show the length of each dinosaur.

	Length in feet:	5	10	15	20	25	30	35	40	45	50	55	60	65	70	75	80	85	90
Tyrannosaurus rex	40 ft.																		
Compsognathus	3 ft.																		
Iguanodon	33 ft.																		
Ankylosaurus	25 ft.																		
Apatosaurus	90 ft.																		
Triceratops	25 ft.																		
Stegosaurus	25 ft.																		
Brachiosaurus	80 ft.																		
Saltopus	2 ft.																		
Giganotosaurus	46 ft.																		
Allosaurus	40 ft.																		

1. Which dinosaur is the longest? _____

2. Which dinosaur is the shortest? _____

Dinosaur Mysteries

Paleontologists study fossils and can tell us so much about the dinosaurs. But, there are some things that the fossils cannot tell us.

1. What color were dinosaurs?

Were they green and yellow? Or were they brown and gray? Did they have spots or stripes? Were they bright red or dark black? Paleontologists do not know for sure! Some believe the dinosaurs were as colorful as the snakes and lizards we see today. Most likely, the dinosaurs were all different colors. And some were camouflaged so that they could blend with their surroundings.

2. What kinds of sounds did dinosaurs make?

Did they bellow like an elephant or roar like a lion? Did they bark like a seal or hiss like a snake? Did they growl, grunt, or honk? Paleontologists study the size and shape of the dinosaur's head and body, and then guess what sounds the dinosaur made.

4. Were dinosaurs warm-blooded or cold-blooded?

Paleontologists first thought that dinosaurs were cold-blooded animals. Cold-blooded reptiles, like crocodiles and lizards, cannot control their body temperature. They must lay in the sun to warm up their blood.

Now, many paleontologists believe that most dinosaurs were warm-blooded, just like humans and birds. Warm-blooded creatures keep their blood warm no matter what the outside temperature. Very large warm-blooded animals must be able to cool down when they get hot. Some large dinosaurs may have used the plates and sails on their back and head to cool down.

3. How long did a dinosaur live?

Did a dinosaur live 10 years? 25 years? 75 years? Paleontologists do not know. Many paleontologists believe that some dinosaurs may have lived to be over 100 years old.

Dinosaur Wordsearch

Find each of the following words.

PTERANODON
SALTOPUS
QUADRUPED
TYRANNOSAURUS REX
COMPSOGNATHUS
TRICERATOPS
APATOSAURUS
CARNIVORE

DINOSAUR
GIGANOTOSAURUS
EXTINCT
ALLOSAURUS
ANKLYOSAURUS
PREHISTORIC
ICHTHYOSAURUS
HERBIVORE

BRACHIOSAURUS
PALEONTOLOGIST
IGUANODON
BIPED
STEGOSAURUS
PLESIOSAURUS
FOSSIL
DIG

```
Q R A P I C H T H Y O S A U R U S O U D
X D I N O S A U R T R I C E R A T O P S
T X S L K P L E S I O S A U R U S E Y O
Y I H R P Y I I O P H E R B I V O R E F
R B I P E D L Y I G U A N O D O N U P O
A U S A L E A O P A C Q E I B I P P E S
N G A L O E P H S T L A A X E P I I U S
N I L E E S A E P A E L R U T X S N O I
O G T O N T T R T Q U R A N D I T T U L
S A O N T E O B E U G R A S I R N I O I
A N P T O G S I R A E T U N A V U C N H
U O U O L O A V A D S P H S O U O P T C
R T S L O S U A N R H T I I T D R R E S
U O D O G A R R O U O P P T T A O U E D
S S O G I U U E D P I G A U N O D N S N
R A S I S R S S A E A L L O S A U R U S
E U S S T U U N D P R E H I S T O I C
X R S T U S S C O M P S O G N A T H U S
C U B R A C H I O S A U R U S A P A A R
R S V T E U T S U P R E H I S T O R I C
```

Let's Talk About Dinosaurs

Do you wish dinosaurs were still living today? Why or why not?

How would you convince your friends and family that it is a good idea to bring back the dinosaurs?

Where is the best place to hide a dinosaur in your school or neighborhood?

What would you feed a hungry dinosaur?

How could you move a dinosaur from New York to Los Angeles?

How would you brush Tyrannosaurus rex's teeth?

Pretend each member of your family is a dinosaur. What dinosaur would each family member be?

How would you protect yourself from a hungry dinosaur?

Where would you least likely find a dinosaur?

Could Triceratops have been black and white striped, like a zebra? Why or why not?

Could you keep a dinosaur in a zoo? Why or why not?

How would you take care of a baby dinosaur?

1	T
2	C
3	I
4	F
5	O
6	X
7	R
8	A
9	E
10	G
11	Q
12	U
13	J
14	N
15	B
16	K
17	M
18	S
19	V
20	H
21	L
22	P
23	D
24	Z
25	W
26	Y

Solve the math problems and then substitute a letter for each number on the red line below to discover the dinosaur.

I was the second dinosaur discovered and named. I had a hard thumb spike on each hand.

$$1 \atop +2 \qquad 5 \atop +5 \qquad 9 \atop +3 \qquad 6 \atop +2 \qquad 7 \atop +7 \qquad 3 \atop +2 \qquad 12 \atop +11 \qquad 1 \atop +4 \qquad 12 \atop +2$$

___ ___ ___ ___ ___ ___ ___ ___ ___

This was my original name means "thunder lizard".

$$5 \atop \times 3 \quad 1 \atop \times 7 \quad 3 \atop +2 \quad 2 \atop \times 7 \quad 1 \atop +0 \quad 5 \atop \times 1 \quad 12 \atop +6 \quad 5 \atop +3 \quad 4 \atop \times 3 \quad 4 \atop +3 \quad 6 \atop +6 \quad 9 \atop \times 2$$

___ ___ ___ ___ ___ ___ ___ ___ ___ ___ ___ ___

I was named for my unusual backbone; my vertebrae was lighter than those of other dinosaurs.

$$13 \atop -5 \quad 3 \atop \times 7 \quad 22 \atop -1 \quad 9 \atop -4 \quad 9 \atop +9 \quad 4 \atop \times 2 \quad 6 \atop \times 2 \quad 14 \atop -7 \quad 7 \atop +5 \quad 6 \atop +3$$

___ ___ ___ ___ ___ ___ ___ ___ ___ ___

I walked on two legs, had a 6-foot long skull, and a brain the size of a banana.

$$5 \atop +5 \quad 6 \atop -3 \quad 6 \atop +4 \quad 2 \atop +6 \quad 7 \atop +7 \quad 10 \atop -5 \quad 4 \atop -3 \quad 1 \atop +4 \quad 9 \atop +9 \quad 10 \atop -2 \quad 10 \atop +2 \quad 4 \atop +3 \quad 6 \atop +6 \quad 18 \atop -0$$

___ ___ ___ ___ ___ ___ ___ ___ ___ ___ ___ ___ ___ ___

I was a small, lightly-built dinosaur that walked on two legs. I had hollow bones and a long head with dozens of small, sharp teeth.

$$9 \atop \times 2 \quad 12 \atop -4 \quad 3 \atop \times 7 \quad 1 \atop -0 \quad 3 \atop +2 \quad 11 \atop +11 \quad 9 \atop +3 \quad 15 \atop +3$$

___ ___ ___ ___ ___ ___ ___ ___

I was about the size of a bus, but my head was about the size of a horse's head.

$$12 \atop +6 \quad 15 \atop -14 \quad 5 \atop +4 \quad 3 \atop +7 \quad 8 \atop -3 \quad 6 \atop \times 3 \quad 4 \atop \times 2 \quad 14 \atop -2 \quad 5 \atop +2 \quad 6 \atop \times 2 \quad 9 \atop +9$$

___ ___ ___ ___ ___ ___ ___ ___ ___ ___ ___

Cut-Out Apatosaurus

1. Cut on the solid black lines.
2. Fold on the dotted black lines.

3. Lock and tape the legs together.
4. Add tape to the tail for balance.

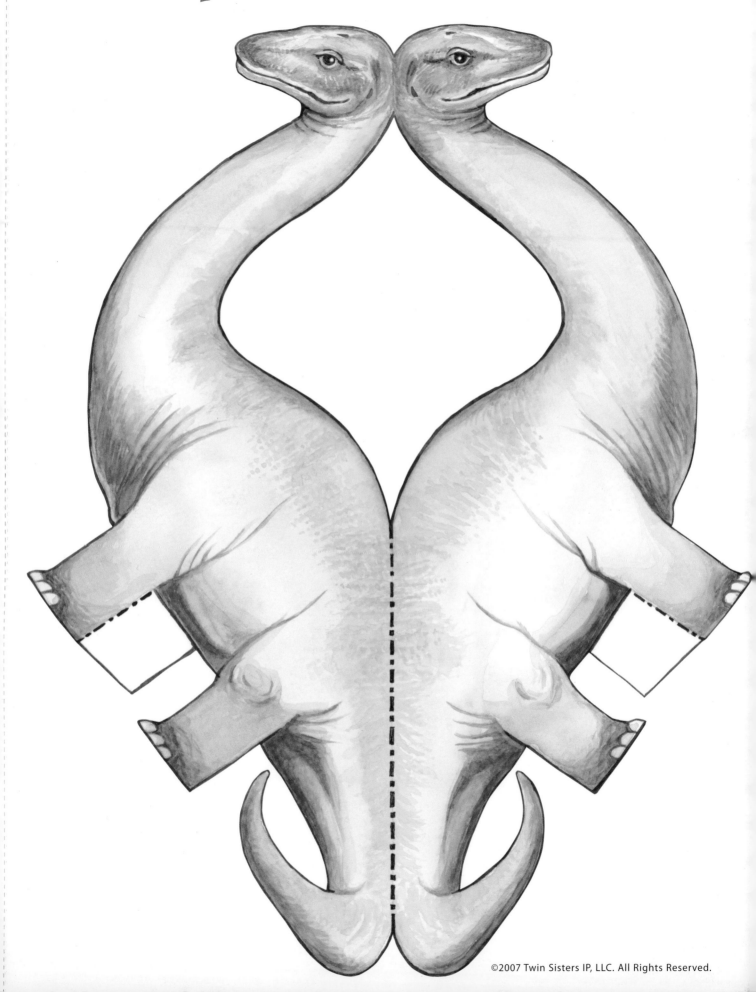

This page was intentionally left blank for the
Cut-Out Iguanodon activity to be completed.

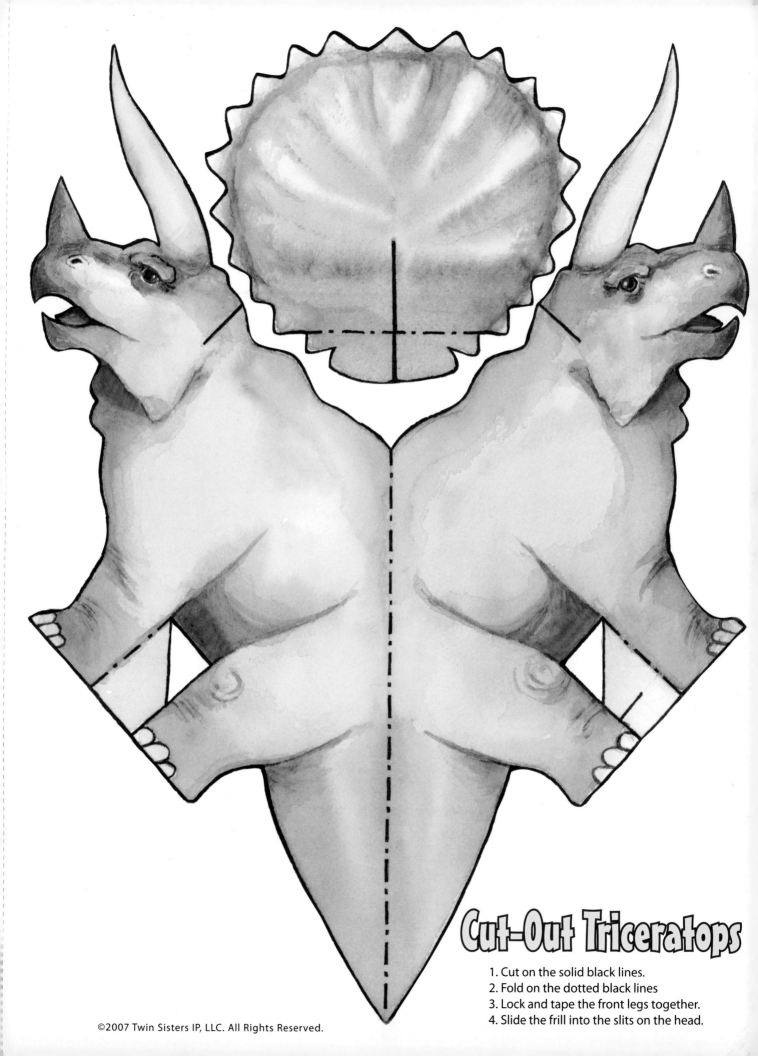

Cut-Out Triceratops

1. Cut on the solid black lines.
2. Fold on the dotted black lines
3. Lock and tape the front legs together.
4. Slide the frill into the slits on the head.

This page was intentionally left blank for the
Cut-Out Iguanodon activity to be completed.

Cut-Out Stegosaurus and Anklyosaurus

1. Cut on the solid black lines.
2. Fold on the dotted black lines.
3. Lock and tape the front legs together.

4. Cut out the additional plates and spikes.
5. Glue or tape the plates onto both sides of the Stegosaurus body.

6. Glue or tape the spikes onto both sides of its tail.

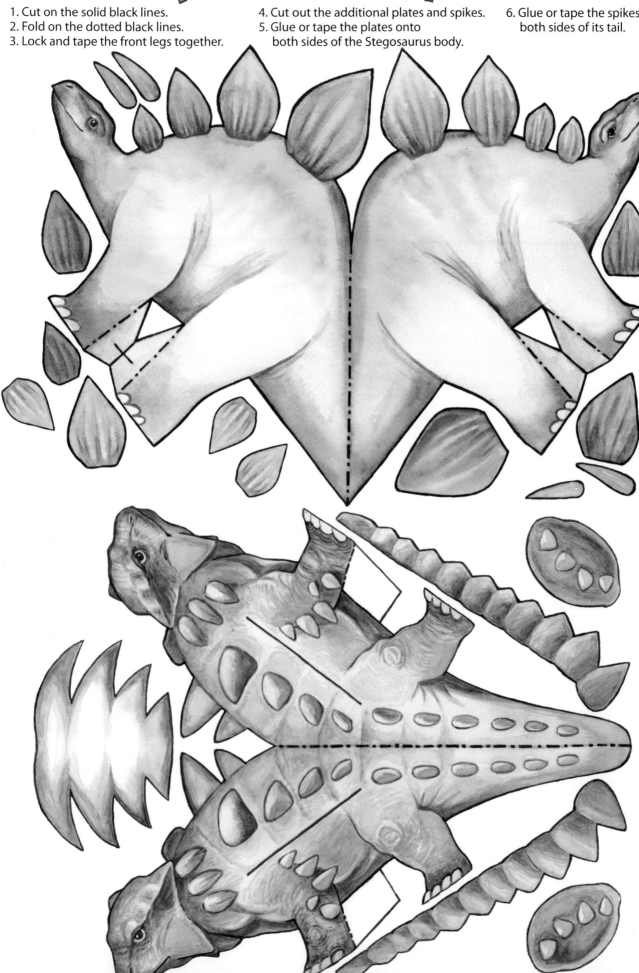

This page was intentionally left blank for the
Cut-Out Iguanodon activity to be completed.